NORTH CENTRAL ILLINOIS
ORNITHOLOGICAL SOCIETY
813 No. Main St.
Rockford, Ill. 61103

Contributed by:—

Milton W. Mahlburg 1947

The author art Williams
was formerly with the Museum
of Natural History in Cleveland Ohio.

D1272041

EASTERN TURKEY

*Collected and mounted by Rufus K. Winslow about 1840,
in attitude shown in Audubon's famous painting.*

SCIENTIFIC PUBLICATIONS OF
THE CLEVELAND MUSEUM OF NATURAL HISTORY — VOLUME X

BULLETIN NUMBER 2 — THE KIRTLAND SOCIETY

ISSUED JUNE, 1950

Birds

of the

Cleveland Region

A Check List of Species Reported
within approximately 30 miles of
the Cleveland Public Square

EDITED BY

ARTHUR B. WILLIAMS, PH. D.

NORTH CENTRAL ILLINOIS
ORNITHOLOGICAL SOCIETY
813 No. Main St.
Rockford, Ill. 61103

THE CLEVELAND MUSEUM OF NATURAL HISTORY
2717 EUCLID AVENUE, CLEVELAND, OHIO

BIRDS OF THE CLEVELAND REGION

———

Table of Contents

Introduction

By ARTHUR B. WILLIAMS

AMONG Clevelanders there has always been a lively interest in the bird life of our surrounding forests, fields and waters. The early pioneers who developed the infant city in the wilderness, in the years immediately following the first surveys of 1796, had an intimate acquaintance with the wild turkey and the passenger pigeon. They were familiar with the great flocks of migratory waterfowl which in spring and in fall blanketed the extensive marsh lands which then existed at the mouth of the Cuyahoga River—in those days right at Cleveland's front door. Many of these birds represented a welcome source of food supply, and every young man was a hunter.

Dr. Jared P. Kirtland, writing 54 years later[*], gives a picture of the bird life of those times. Said he:

"The rapacious family of birds was very strongly represented. The Bald Eagle visited the premises of almost every farmer during cold weather. The Golden Eagle was not uncommon, particularly along the shores of the Lake. Of the former a few remain at the present day; the latter has nearly or quite forsaken its former locations.

The Red-tailed, Red-shouldered, Broad-winged and Cooper's Hawks, might, in early days, be found nesting on almost every acre of the Western Reserve, and during the summer the beautiful Swallow-tailed Hawk visited here in considerable numbers in pursuit of its favorite food. It might be seen moving in graceful circles at no great height, watching for the garter snake that then infested our meadows.

Wild Geese, Swans, Ducks and wading birds literally swarmed about every lake, pond and creek, during Spring and Autumn. Many species also bred in the Reserve.

The flocks of Wild Turkeys were more common and numerous than are those of the tame variety of the present day. The Partridge and Quail were not so very abundant. The

---

[*] Family Visitor, Vol. 1, No. 1, January 3, 1850.

Pileated Woodcock was found on every dry tree. The sound of his heavy blows and loud note were heard on all sides; and many a decaying trunk was literally demolished by his labors.

Turkey Buzzards and Ravens collected in numerous flocks about every dead carcase—while the crow was less abundant than it is in more recent times.

The Crow Black Bird might be found nesting in almost every hollow and cavity in decaying trees. His habits in constructing his nest were different from his kin in the New England States, where it builds its nest exclusively on some fork of a limb of a live tree near its extremity.

The Robin, Blue Bird, Thrush, Cat-bird, and many small species, have, perhaps, increased as our fields and orchards have been extended and afforded them favorite resorts.''

Since the early days of which Kirtland wrote, stupendous changes in the natural environment have taken place, profoundly affecting the bird life of the region. During this period also, bird study as a recreational hobby has developed to the point where it has produced a remarkable number of enthusiastic followers who are expert in the identification of birds in the field. All such persons are keenly aware that changes in the character of certain localities formerly affording sanctuary to many species of birds about Cleveland have come about even of late years, making many areas unsuitable to bird life. Nowhere is this more apparent than along the Lake Erie shore. Shorebirds are finding continually less and less to attract them within the limits covered by this list.

In reviewing the records of the various species it is all too apparent that certain birds have been decreasing in numbers in the region in the last 150 years. Some have dropped out of the picture altogether. Those which have gone are the wild turkey, Carolina paroquet, Eskimo curlew, trumpeter swan, passenger pigeon and swallow-tailed kite. Shorebirds have been decreasing in numbers, but changes in habitat may account for much of this. Birds that have increased are those which have adapted themselves to the presence of man, his clearings, buildings and practices. Such are the robin, house wren, cardinal, meadowlark, bobolink, killdeer, and others.

During this interval of over 150 years, although students of birds have been by no means lacking in numbers or in interest

2

in and about Cleveland, no inclusive and authoritative list of the birds of the Cleveland region has ever been published. The nearest approach to such a list is that of Ingersoll and Chubb, referred to on page 187.

Meanwhile a vast amount of material bearing on the bird life of the Cleveland region has accumulated in scattered books, magazines, articles, reports, and personal records. Especially is this true of the records contained in the *Cleveland Bird Calendar*. This mimeographed bulletin alone, now in its 46th year, has preserved thousands of records concerning the birds of this region. It was started in 1905 by Professor Francis H. Herrick of the Department of Biology of Western Reserve University. Until 1931 it was carried on by Dr. Herrick and a few friends, particularly Professor W. H. Hulme and Professor C. M. Finfrock.

In 1931 the *Calendar* became the joint project of the Department of Biology of the University, and the Cleveland Bird Club. Dr. S. C. Kendeigh of the Department of Biology represented both organizations as editor. Under this arrangement the scope of the *Calendar* was greatly enlarged and its field of usefulness correspondingly increased.

Following Dr. Kendeigh's removal from Cleveland in 1938, Dr. John W. Aldrich, then Curator of Ornithology of the Cleveland Museum of Natural History, was appointed editor by a committee of the Bird Club, and the Museum replaced the University as a sponsor of the *Calendar*. Upon Dr. Aldrich's removal to Washington in 1941, Dr. Arthur B. Williams, Curator of Education in the Museum, was appointed editor by a committee of the Cleveland Bird Club.

In 1943, by agreement between the Cleveland Bird Club and the Kirtland Bird Club, an organization affiliated with the Museum of Natural History, the publication of the *Calendar* became the responsibility of the Kirtland Bird Club, in co-operation with the Cleveland Bird Club; the Museum continuing its sponsorship of the *Calendar,* and Dr. Williams continuing as editor.

It is the purpose of this check list to bring all these records together; to evaluate and consolidate them; and to present the results in the form of a simple statement of facts which will summarize our present knowledge of the occurrence and local distribution of each species of bird that has been authoritatively recorded from the Cleveland region.

Acknowledgments

T HE WORK of compiling the list and making the information available has been done largely by members of the Kirtland Bird Club. The plan of the work was first organized by Dr. Harry C. Oberholser in 1943. Inasmuch as it was a spare-time job, it took four years to complete the careful reading of all the books, magazines and published reports that might have in them possible references to the ornithology of the Cleveland region. The reduction of these records to systematic accounts was begun in 1948. The editing of them occupied odd moments of most of 1949. A few records only are included beyond January 1, 1949.

Members or former members of the Kirtland Bird Club who contributed time and effort to the production of the list are:

John W. Aldrich	H. C. Oberholser
Vera Carrothers	Margaret E. Perner
Edith Dobbins	Jerry Piskac
H. C. Dobbins	Marjorie Ramisch
Elsie C. Erickson	Raymond Roth
James S. Findley	William E. Scheele
W. Earl Godfrey	Ray Smiley
Carl F. Hamann	Mildred Stewart
Raymond W. Hill	Robert S. Smith
Mrs. Luella Literaty	Clark Tefft
Nadine Literaty	Harold E. Wallin
Margarette E. Morse	Lida H. Whittier
Donald L. Newman	Arthur B. Williams

Others who rendered special services are Mrs. William E. Hanna, who did much detail work for the editor; Dr. Lynds Jones of Oberlin, who was frequently consulted on early records; John E. Lieftinck of Akron, who persuaded us to recognize the Akron Lakes as a part of our region, and who provided many records from these lakes; Frank M. Phelps of Elyria, who provided much helpful information from the western part of our region; and Mrs. Florence Wise, who copied the records from the Ohio Catalogue of Birds in the Cleveland Museum of Natural History collections.

To Dr. John W. Aldrich of the U. S. Fish and Wildlife Service, a former member of the Kirtland Bird Club, we are greatly indebted for the checking of all scientific names. The help of Miss Mildred Stewart of the Cleveland Public Library in looking up certain records in early publications; and of the Western Reserve Historical Society in unearthing biographical material relative to some of Cleveland's early naturalists, is greatly appreciated.

The special thanks of the editor are due Mrs. Lida H. Whittier for her careful checking of the copy and discriminating help with the editing of it.

The Check List

THIS CHECK LIST makes possible at least a tentative answer to certain basic questions regarding bird life in the vicinity of Cleveland, Ohio. These are:

What species of birds have been reliably reported as occurring in the Cleveland region?

How common or uncommon are they?

At what time of year may one expect to see them?

Where may they be looked for?

Where, and in what manner, do they nest?

Questions such as these, simple as they may appear to be, can be adequately answered only on the basis of many years of observation on the part of many people, and the conscientious preservation of these observations in the shape of written records. In these respects we are indeed fortunate, as we have indicated, in having a long history of bird observations in this area to draw upon as source material for this work.

We believe this to be the first local list to attempt to supply quantitative information on some of the birds inhabiting a given area. This has been made possible because of the painstaking field work which certain members and friends of the Kirtland Bird Club have been carrying on since 1931. Including 1949, this work has involved the study of no less than 51 separate typical breeding habitats, totaling in all, 1539.4 acres of land. These studies have been developed by 51 different people who have devoted 133 seasons of effort to their projects. The breeding activities of 9543 pairs of birds of 115 different species nesting in our region (See page 202) have thus been brought under close observation, and the results largely made available for study through publication in the *Audubon Magazine* and *Audubon Field Notes.*

Also included are several seasons of weekly studies of wintering waterfowl along the Lake Erie shore, from the mouth of Rocky River to East 140th Street.

The Herrick Ornithological Club (See page 191) conducted a series of such studies from November 1, 1939, to April 1, 1940, and again from December 22, 1940, to February 23, 1941. The following winter (October 5, 1941, to March 29, 1942) a more completely organized study of the same area was made by the Kirtland Bird Club under the leadership of Ralph A. O'Reilly, Jr., assisted by 14 other club members. The extensive tabulated results of these studies, published in the *Cleveland Bird Calendar,* are a tribute to the enthusiasm and persistence with which this group carried through these schedules of weekly observations in the bleakest part of the city, and the coldest parts of the day and year.

Check lists such as this have been made for numerous localities. Two of special interest to us are "The Birds of the Chicago Region" (1934), by Edward R. Ford, Colin C. Sanborn and C. Blair Coursen, published by the Chicago Academy of Sciences; and "The Birds of Lucas County" (Ohio) (1940), by Louis W. Campbell, published by the Toledo Zoological Society.

Such lists are useful to the beginner in bird study as a guide to what he may expect to see or not see in the region covered. To the more advanced student the list is a convenient standard against which to check his own observations, and a challenge to duplicate, or better, some of the records set forth therein. Thus he may be in a position to make important additions to the present knowledge of the bird life of the region.

We hope that this list may be of value to the professional ornithologist as an aid to the study of the abundance, distribution and migration of birds throughout the country.

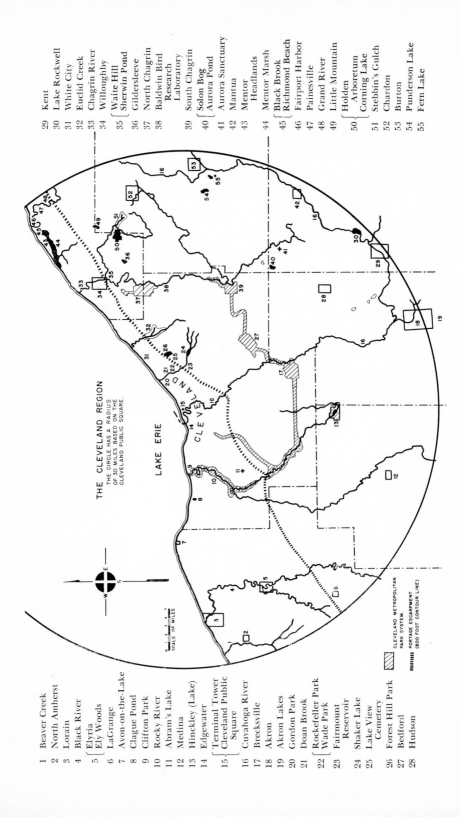

THE CLEVELAND REGION

THE CIRCLE HAS A RADIUS
OF 30 MILES BASED ON THE
CLEVELAND PUBLIC SQUARE.

LAKE ERIE

CLEVELAND

SCALE OF MILES

CLEVELAND METROPOLITAN
PARK SYSTEM.

PORTAGE ESCARPMENT
(800 FOOT CONTOUR LINE)

1   Beaver Creek
2   North Amherst
3   Lorain
4   Black River
5 { Elyria
    Ely Woods
6   LaGrange
7   Avon-on-the-Lake
8   Clague Pond
9   Clifton Park
10 Rocky River
11 Abram's Lake
12 Medina
13 Hinckley (Lake)
14 Edgewater
15 { Terminal Tower
    Cleveland Public
    Square
16 Cuyahoga River
17 Brecksville
18 Akron
19 Akron Lakes
20 Gordon Park
21 Doan Brook
22 { Rockefeller Park
    Wade Park
23 Fairmount
    Reservoir
24 Shaker Lake
25 Lake View
    Cemetery
26 Forest Hill Park
27 Bedford
28 Hudson

29 Kent
30 Lake Rockwell
31 White City
32 Euclid Creek
33 Chagrin River
34 Willoughby
35 { Waite Hill
    Sherwin Pond
36 Gildersleeve
37 North Chagrin
38 Baldwin Bird
    Research
    Laboratory
39 South Chagrin
40 Solon Bog
41 Aurora Pond
42 Aurora Sanctuary
43 Mantua
44 Mentor
    Headlands
45 Mentor Marsh
46 Black Brook
47 Richmond Beach
48 Fairport Harbor
49 Painesville
50 Grand River
51 Little Mountain
52 { Holden
    Arboretum
53 Corning Lake
54 Stebbin's Gulch
55 Chardon
    Burton
    Punderson Lake
    Fern Lake

The Cleveland Region

For the purposes of this list, the Cleveland region is defined as all territory lying in any direction within 30 miles of the Cleveland Public Square (See map). This obviously cannot be considered as a hard and fast limit, but an approximate one insofar as marginal territory may be concerned. To the south we have allowed for a bulge of approximately 10 miles to take in the Akron Lakes, which topographically belong to the region (See page 193, Akron Lakes).

Compared with some other local lists, the Cleveland region, thus defined, is a relatively small area. Yet it includes about 60 miles of the southern shore of Lake Erie, in which lie the harbors of Fairport, Cleveland and Lorain. It includes most of the drainage system of the Black River; all of that of Rocky River, including both East and West Branches; the entire drainage of the Cuyahoga, except a small portion of its headwater streams; all of the drainage of the Chagrin River, including both East and Aurora Branches; and approximately 14 miles of the Grand River from a point just east of Painesville to the river mouth at Fairport. It includes about 1650 square miles of land and about 1180 square miles of Lake Erie—a body of water whose bird life we may explore more thoroughly some day than has been possible up to the present time.

Familiar place names on or near the perimeter of this semicircle are Fairport, Painesville, Chardon, Burton, Mantua, Kent, Akron, Medina, Litchfield, LaGrange, Elyria, North Amherst and Lorain. The City of Cleveland occupies its mid portion. Included is all of Cuyahoga County and portions of the adjoining counties of Lake, Geauga, Portage, Summit, Medina and Lorain.

The topography of this region is varied, and this contributes much to the interest of bird study within its limits. It so happens that Cleveland sits astride the boundary line between the Appalachian Plateaus Province (to the east) and the Great Central Lowlands Province (to the west). This is no imaginary line, but in most places is a prominent feature of the landscape. It is known to geologists as the Portage Escarpment. To the east and south are rolling hills, cut by ravines, gorges and river valleys. To the north and west are lake plains and till plains forming relatively level country.

The rivers mentioned have developed, in some cases, extensive flood plains. Coinciding with our 30-mile boundary to the south, the higher lands form the watershed between the Lake Erie (St. Lawrence Basin) drainage, and the Ohio (Mississippi Basin) drainage.

This change in topography as between east and west also marks a change in climate between Atlantic Coastal and Interior Lowlands, which is reflected in significant changes in plant and animal life. The location is such that it becomes a veritable ecological crossroads. Inspection of the map will make these features plain.

The original vegetation of the region was as varied as its topography. Following the retreat of the glacial ice some 25,000 years ago, a succession of boreal forest types occupied the land until the climate became such that the deciduous forest could compete with the evergreen trees. Then a gradual replacement of the evergreens by the broad-leaved trees began, which in our day has all but eliminated the forests of the colder climates. The few remaining hemlocks are remnants of those forests, as are such places as Little Mountain and Fern Lake (See page 195).

When the City of Cleveland was first mapped in the wilderness in 1796, the dominant forest type over all the uplands was beech and sugar maple. Included within this forest in certain wet locations were upland swamp forests dominated by American elm, red maple and black ash. Other wet locations supported dense stands of pin oak. On the Lake Plain were lowland swamp forests of American elm, silver maple and black ash. On the old lake beaches black oak, tulip, white ash and chestnut dominated the scene. To the south were great forests of oak, hickory and chestnut, in which white oak was one of the most common species. The ravines and the escarpment edge were dark with hemlocks, and there were here and there small groves of white pine. In the river bottomlands sycamores, cottonwoods, and black walnuts grew to giant size.*

---

* The Native Forests of Cuyahoga County, Ohio, by Arthur B. Williams, Scientific Publication of the Cleveland Museum of Natural History, Vol. IX, 1949.

There are now but a few remnants of these old forests left in the region. Greater Cleveland, with its solidly built-up business sections; its large manufacturing areas and its far-flung suburban communities east, west and south, occupies a large section of the area to which we have limited this list, thus reducing greatly the areas which are attractive to birds.

This means that, although there is still some open country to be found within our boundaries, a large part of the land is devoted to the sites of cities, towns and villages, including manufacturing plants, mills, airports, railway yards, shipping and other industries. Compared with these evidences of human occupancy, farming takes a relatively minor position.

The region is situated on that portion of the Atlantic Flyway used in fall by ducks and geese coming from western Quebec and Ontario, Hudson Bay, and northwest Canada, as described by Lincoln.* Certain routes tributary to this flyway converge toward the western end of Lake Erie, thence turn directly east to cross northern Ohio on the way to wintering grounds along the southern Atlantic coast.

The Lake Erie shore line also constitutes a definite migration route for many of the smaller species of birds.

Our regional limits necessitate the omission from detailed consideration of the regions of Sandusky Bay, Pymatuning Reservoir, and Mosquito Creek—places to which Cleveland bird students constantly go. Here occur concentrations of water birds during migration periods, such as we no longer see within our regional boundaries. Our local records now include only the fringes, so to speak, of these great flocks.

Yet there are, within our limits, some choice places for the study of bird life. Since these are constantly referred to in the following pages, it will be useful to identify them at the back of the book so that extended reference to them here will be unnecessary (See pages 193-197).

---

* The Waterfowl Flyways of North America, by Frederick C. Lincoln, U. S. Department of Agriculture Circular No. 342, January 1935, pp. 3-4.

9

Definitions and Explanations

THE ORDER in which the species are listed is that of the Check List of the American Ornithologists' Union, 4th Edition, and supplements. The scientific names have been brought up to date as far as possible, and have been revised by Dr. John W. Aldrich of the U. S. Fish and Wildlife Service.

The necessity for the employment of subspecific names in many cases in this list poses a problem in treatment which, in the present state of our knowledge, is difficult of satisfactory solution.

In the following pages we have adopted the policy of using subspecific names when specimens of the subspecies, taken in the region, are at hand; or, in the absence of specimens, when the region is included in the breeding range or usual migration route of such subspecies.

When two or more subspecies may possibly occur in the region, and no specimens are at hand, the species name is used.

Rare or accidental visitors, not recognizable in the field as subspecies, in the absence of specimens, are listed under species names.

In all cases of important records, references are given. If, in such cases, no reference appears, it is understood that its source is the *Cleveland Bird Calendar*. An exception is made in the case of first and last dates of occurrence. These may be based upon *Cleveland Bird Calendar* records or other sources. When no specific locality is given, it is understood that the Cleveland region, as defined on page 7, is indicated.

The status of the species in the region—that is, its abundance or rarity—is, of course, a matter of opinion based on experience. We hope the following definitions may make clear the terminology adopted for this important information.

In this connection, one needs to keep in mind the fact that most birds prefer certain kinds of habitats, and, during the breeding season at least, are usually not found outside the limits of their habitat preference. In such places they may become locally abundant or common, though rare or absent elsewhere.

Definitions

ABUNDANT—Present in such numbers that the bird can hardly fail to be noticed; requiring no effort or special search to find it. Example—robin.

COMMON—Present in lesser numbers than indicated by "abundant", yet so numerous that it can always be found by looking for it in its preferred habitat. Example—catbird.

NOT UNCOMMON—Present in lesser numbers than indicated by "common", not always to be found when searched for, but persistent effort will usually result in finding it. Example—pileated woodpecker.

UNCOMMON—Present in such small numbers, either as a permanent resident, migrant, or occasional visitor, as to make its appearance uncertain or irregular. Examples—ruffed grouse, upland plover.

RARE—Present only occasionally and so limited in occurrence that its appearance cannot be predicted with certainty. Examples—red crossbill, Bohemian waxwing.

ACCIDENTAL—Present so irregularly as to be accounted for only as the result of accidental causes. Examples—gannet, little gull.

Terms expressing relative abundance may be limited by locality (as hooded warbler—a summer resident species), or by time (as olive-backed thrush—a migrant). It may be useful also to define a few other terms used in the list, such as the following:

THE LETTERS CMNH stand for Cleveland Museum of Natural History.

AVERAGE—The word "average" as applied to dates of arrival or departure means average *first* or average *last* date over a period of years. Very early or very late dates, although given for the sake of the record, are relatively unimportant, since they are not typical of regular migratory movements. The height of abundance or time when the species is regularly present in maximum numbers is far more significant.

PERMANENT RESIDENT—The species is present throughout the year, although migration may also take place. Example—blue jay.

SUMMER RESIDENT—Present as a *breeding* species throughout the summer, as well as a migrant in spring and fall. Example—redstart.

MIGRANT—Present only in spring and fall as a transient. More or less regular in occurrence, however. Example—whistling swan, hermit thrush.

VISITOR—Present more or less as a wanderer. May be regular in occurrence (as tree sparrow), or irregular (as Iceland gull).

11

W$_E$ MAKE NO APOLOGY for the inclusion of many sight records herein. The editor is of the opinion that the time has long since passed when a good sight record of a clearly recognizable species must be ignored because the bird in question was not shot and reported "collected" as a specimen duly identified by a professional ornithologist.

Modern bird study in the field has produced, in the case of many amateurs, a truly amazing facility in the identification of living birds in their native haunts. Equipped with modern binoculars and "spotting" telescopes; aided by authoritative handbooks; and qualified by much field experience, many amateurs have developed techniques and skills in the identification of birds in the field that were unknown a generation or so ago. Their carefully considered reports, we think, are worthy of credence. Good examples of such reporting in this book are the records of the yellow-crowned night heron (page 20) and the little gull (page 70).

Fortunately, Cleveland has a remarkably able corps of amateur bird observers, many of whose names appear frequently in connection with the records given herein.

W$_E$ PREDICT a long period of usefulness for this list. While we cannot claim that it is by any means complete at the present time, we can say that it does represent a careful compilation and interpretation of all available records. Considering the number of people who are, or have been, students of birds in the Cleveland region, we are reasonably sure that there must be many an interesting or important record which has not come to our attention. The editor, or any officer or member of the Kirtland Bird Club, will welcome at any time suggestions or important additional records from anyone interested in making a future edition of this list more complete and authoritative than the first issue.

Holding strictly to the answering of the questions set forth on page 5 has precluded descriptive writing. It has been difficult at times to keep descriptive matter out, particularly in connection with nesting data. The opportunity to do this is reserved, we hope, for some future publication on the nesting habits of the birds of the Cleveland region, a project in which the Kirtland Bird Club solicits the cooperation of all bird students within the region.

NOTE—A historical summary of ornithological interest in the region will be found on pages 185 to 192.

Birds of the Cleveland Region

Order GAVIIFORMES

Family GAVIIDAE (Loons)

GREATER COMMON LOON—Gavia immer immer (Brünnich)

Two forms of the common loon (this and the following) occur in the region. Since they are practically indistinguishable in the field, we include here all records for "common loon" not verified by specimens, which we have.

STATUS—Common migrant; uncommon winter visitor.

EARLIEST SPRING DATE—March 1, 1947. PEAK OF NUMBERS—April 15-20. LATEST—May 28, 1944.

EARLIEST FALL DATE—October 1, 1932. PEAK OF NUMBERS—October 25-November 16. LATEST—December 31, 1944.

Unusual records are: January 11(7), January 26(4), February 11(1). Also one seen on Pippin Lake (a small lake northeast of Kent) July 21, 1946.

HABITAT AND DISTRIBUTION—During April and early May, and again in October, migratory loons are reported regularly, not only on Lake Erie, but also on many inland ponds and lakes. Usually larger numbers are seen in fall than in spring. In winter they are commonly seen singly or in small groups along the Lake Erie shore all the way from Fairport to Lorain in our region. Since loons are birds of the open waters, it is probable that their numbers on Lake Erie during migration may be far greater than our records indicate.

In the collection of the CMNH are 3 specimens of this larger, northerly breeding form—a female taken at Cleveland April 15, 1940; a female at Avon-on-the-Lake December 30, 1948; and a female at Willoughby November 6, 1939.

LESSER COMMON LOON—Gavia immer elasson Bishop

This is the smaller, more southerly breeding form. See greater common loon (above) for dates and discussion of status and habitat.

In the collections of the CMNH are two specimens of this form —a female taken at Cleveland April 23, 1924; and a male taken at Willowick December 23, 1926.

RED-THROATED LOON—Gavia stellata (Pontoppidan)

STATUS—Rare or accidental migrant.

The occasional records of this northern species which we have indicate that it may be expected to appear here during either the spring or fall migration periods. Single individuals have been reported as follows: Elyria, April 1935 (F. M. Phelps); Cleveland, April 30, 1880 (Chubb 1880); Painesville, 1915 (Hersey 1917:286); Gordon Park, May 14, 1939 (B. P. Bole, Jr.); Lake Shore east of Gordon Park, November 1, 1938 (J. W. Aldrich, B. P. Bole, Jr., A. B. Williams); Gordon Park, November 30, December 2, 3, 1947 (A. B. Williams); Edgewater Park, December 7, 1947 (M. Owen Davies). A single bird was also reported as present on the Oberlin reservoir in the spring of 1948 (Lynds Jones). The Elyria record is especially interesting. Frank M. Phelps writes: "In April 1935 a farmer near Elyria caught a grounded loon, which was placed in the fountain pool in Ely Park in the center of town. I was quite surprised to find it a small red-throated loon. It could be readily studied at very close range."

Order COLYMBIFORMES

Family COLYMBIDAE (Grebes)

HOLBOELL'S GREBE—Colymbus grisegena holböllii (Reinhardt)

STATUS—Rare migrant; rare winter visitor.

EARLIEST FALL DATE—September 16, 1945.

LATEST SPRING DATE—May 11, 1913.

Although we have records of the occurrence of this grebe from September 16 to May 11, it has been most frequently reported in December and April.

HABITAT AND DISTRIBUTION—Chiefly seen on Lake Erie, although there are records for Corning Lake, Hinckley Lake, Sherwin Pond, and Forest Hill Park pond.

HORNED GREBE—Colymbus auritus Linnaeus

STATUS—Common migrant; more or less regular winter visitor.

EARLIEST SPRING DATE — March 2, 1935. AVERAGE — April 15.

LATEST — May 15, 1943. An unusual record is that of a pair reported on Hinckley Lake June 2, 1941 by W. E. Scheele.

EARLIEST FALL DATE—August 16, 1949. AVERAGE LAST—November 20. A few commonly winter along the Lake Erie shore, as many December, January and February records indicate.

HABITAT AND DISTRIBUTION—Along the Lake Erie shore from Fairport to Lorain in our region, and on inland lakes and ponds, this small grebe is likely to be seen in some numbers during the heavy migration periods of April and November. Flocks of 50 or more have been reported. There are a number of records of grounded grebes of this species being captured alive.

EARED GREBE—Colymbus caspicus californicus (Heermann)

STATUS—Rare and accidental visitor.

We have three records of this western species in our region. One reported at Fairport Harbor April 17, 1926, by F. N. Shankland, who says that identification was made by "several experienced observers." One seen on Corning Lake April 21, 1941, by B. P. Bole, Jr., and collected April 22, 1941 (Godfrey 1943b). One seen on Corning Lake April 24, 1946, by B. P. Bole, Jr., in the same locality as the specimen collected April 22, 1941.

PIED-BILLED GREBE—Podilymbus podiceps podiceps (Linnaeus)

STATUS—Common migrant; common summer resident; occasional in winter.

EARLIEST SPRING DATE—March 1, 1943. PEAK OF NUMBERS—Late March and early April.

LATEST FALL DATE—December 27, 1947. AVERAGE—November 8. Occasional in January and February.

HABITAT AND DISTRIBUTION—In migration may be found on almost any inland pond as well as along the Lake Erie shore. During the breeding season it prefers marshy edges of ponds, cattail or buttonbush swamps, or the borders of lakes overgrown with sedges and grasses. Well distributed throughout the region wherever nesting requirements are satisfied.

NESTING—Nest built of decaying water vegetation, either upon a mat of bent-over flags or rushes, or even floating in shallow water. Buttonbush Bog (Holden Arboretum), June 3, nest, 5 eggs. Corning Lake, nest, 6 eggs, summer of 1941, located within 8 inches of nest of red-winged blackbird containing 4 young; grebe's nest in 1 foot of water, red-wing's nest in cattails directly above grebe's nest. Aurora Bird Sanctuary, July 11, adult feeding 5 young on water; August 8, young now self-sufficient.

Order PELECANIFORMES

Family SULIDAE (Boobies and Gannets)

GANNET—Morus bassanus (Linnaeus)

STATUS—Rare and accidental autumn and winter visitor.

HABITAT AND DISTRIBUTION—Previous to the winter of 1947-8 there were but 3 recorded occurrences of this North Atlantic bird on Lake Erie. These were: 1 captured alive at Fairport Harbor November 2, 1925, banded by E. W. Hadeler of Painesville, photographed by C. M. Shipman of Willoughby, and released; 1 captured by fishermen near the mouth of Beaver Creek November 10, 1929, given to Dr. Lynds Jones of Oberlin, who presented it to the Ohio State Museum; 1 collected by Dr. Carl Tuttle of Berlin Heights, at Cedar Point, approximately November 15, 1931, reported by letter to Dr. Lynds Jones of Oberlin. All of the above were birds in immature plumage.

From December 6, 1947, to January 13, 1948, gannets, ranging in numbers from 1 to 5, were reported by many competent observers almost daily, fishing with the gulls in the small strip of open water near the plant of the Cleveland Electric Illuminating Company on the Lake Erie shore just west of Gordon Park, Cleveland. These birds were all in immature plumage. Two birds in adult plumage were reported August 29, 1948, at Fairport Harbor by George King.

Family PHALACROCORACIDAE (Cormorants)

NORTHERN DOUBLE-CRESTED CORMORANT— Phalacrocorax auritus auritus (Lesson)

STATUS—Not uncommon spring and winter visitor.

EARLIEST FALL DATE—September 25, 1943. Most frequently seen during November, December, January.

LATEST SPRING DATE—May 19, 1946. There is a record of 1 seen at Sandusky June 8, 1947 (Lieftinck); and of an immature bird seen at White City July 6, 1949 (Hill).

HABITAT AND DISTRIBUTION—From late September to mid-May this species has been commonly observed of late years in small numbers (1-9) along the Lake Erie shore, particularly at Fairport

16

Harbor, Gordon Park, and along the breakwater to Rocky River and Lorain. It has occasionally been reported in such inland waters as Hinckley Lake, Aurora Pond and Sherwin Pond.

Order CICONIIFORMES

Family ARDEIDAE (Herons and Bitterns)

EASTERN GREAT BLUE HERON—Ardea herodias herodias Linnaeus

STATUS—Common migrant; not uncommon summer resident; occasional in December, January and February.

EARLIEST SPRING DATE — March 8, 1940 and 1946. AVERAGE — March 23.

Because of the fact that so many great blues linger about the lakes and ponds through October and November, it is difficult, if not impossible, to determine any "last" fall migratory date. There are many December records, and a few in January and February.

HABITAT AND DISTRIBUTION—During migration, and particularly in the fall, may be found along marshy margins of lakes, ponds and streams, including the Lake Erie shore. During the nesting season they are more limited in distribution due to their habit of nesting in colonies.

NESTING—In colonies, usually in large trees, and not far from water where food may be obtained. Within the region, nesting colonies of from 4 to 40 nests have been reported at Novelty, Fullertown, Aurora, Mentor, Streetsboro, Hinckley and LaGrange. Nests are bulky affairs made of good-sized twigs placed in tops, or well up, in large trees, often beech or sugar maple. Often several nests in the same tree. The same nests may be occupied from one year to another. Adults have been observed on nests as early as April 1, some birds apparently incubating. May 13, many egg shells on ground, young birds could be heard in nests. June 3, young birds standing in nests. June 26, young still in nests.

AMERICAN EGRET—Casmerodius albus egretta (Gmelin)

STATUS—Uncommon spring visitor, becoming more common in July and August.

17

EARLIEST SPRING DATE—April 17, 1941. LATEST—May 28, 1944. The fact that birds are reported continuously after June 21 would indicate that this date marks approximately the beginning of the post-breeding wanderings so characteristic of this species.

LATEST FALL DATE—October 16, 1931. Numbers reported build up during June, July and August, decreasing in September and October.

HABITAT AND DISTRIBUTION—Frequents marshy edges of rivers, lakes and ponds. Has been recorded within our region from Chagrin River, Shaker Lakes, North Chagrin, Rocky River, Cuyahoga River at Willow, Aurora, Welshfield, the Akron Lakes, and Beaver Creek. The fact that there is a recently established nesting colony on West Sister Island, Lake Erie (Campbell 1947:461), indicates that this species is on the increase in our neighborhood and that we may expect to see it more frequently in the future than in the more recent past.

SNOWY EGRET—Leucophoyx thula thula (Molina)

STATUS—Rare and accidental fall visitor.

This southern heron has been 7 times reported from our region: Rocky River near Trailside Museum, August 5, 1940, one reported by Harold E. Wallin; Cleveland, August 25, 1889 (Cooke 1911:4); Wingfoot Lake, August 4, 14, 21, 28, 1948, one reported by J. E. Lieftinck; Wingfoot Lake, September 12, 1936, one reported by J. E. Lieftinck; Shaker Lake, October 4, 1936, one reported by Ralph A. O'Reilly, Jr.; Wingfoot Lake, August 3, 20, 1949, two reported by J. E. Lieftinck; Wingfoot Lake, August 28, 1949, one reported by Vera Carrothers.

HABITAT AND DISTRIBUTION—Like other herons this species is a frequenter of the marshy edges of ponds and rivers.

LITTLE BLUE HERON—Florida caerulea caerulea (Linnaeus)

STATUS—Uncommon spring and fall visitor.

EARLIEST SPRING DATE — April 28, 1948. AVERAGE (of 7 May records)—May 18.

LATEST FALL DATE—September 7, 1947.

Spring records vary from April 28 to May 29. Fall records vary from July 24 to September 7. Most frequently seen in

August. J. E. Lieftinck reports a group varying from 4 to 6 in number present on Wingfoot Lake July 27 to August 28, 1948. Greatest number seen at one time, 6. Birds in both immature and adult plumage have been reported.

HABITAT AND DISTRIBUTION — Frequents shores of lakes and ponds, river edges. Reported from Hinckley Lake, Wingfoot Lake, Rocky River, Chagrin River, Grand River, Lake Rockwell, Sherwin Pond, Shaker Lake and Mentor Marsh.

EASTERN GREEN HERON—Butorides virescens virescens (Linnaeus)

STATUS—Common migrant; common summer resident.

EARLIEST SPRING DATE—March 12, 1938. AVERAGE—April 20.

LATEST FALL DATE—November 12, 1947. AVERAGE—October 22.

There is an unusual record of 2 birds seen December 28, 1943, and another of 1 bird January 1, 1942. Heaviest migration is in April and September.

HABITAT AND DISTRIBUTION—Commonly seen about bogs, ponds, and river edges; during migration on almost any body of water in the region.

NESTING—Nest of coarse twigs and sticks in small or large tree, not necessarily near water. June 3, nest, 4 eggs in Buttonbush Bog (Holden Arboretum) about 3 feet above the water. June 22, nest with 5 half-grown young in wild apple tree 15 feet from ground, 30 feet from pond. July 1, nest building begun in elm about 75 feet up, in residential section of Cleveland Heights about a mile from Shaker Lake; incubation period about 3 weeks. May 3, nest construction started with old blue jay's nest as a base in an apple tree in residential section of Shaker Heights; May 7, 4 eggs; May 31, eggs hatched; June 7, young crawl out of nest; June 22, young fly to nearby tree; June 29, young apparently can "do their own fishing" but return to apple tree at night.

BLACK-CROWNED NIGHT HERON — Nycticorax nycticorax hoactli (Gmelin)

STATUS—Uncommon migrant; not uncommon summer resident.

EARLIEST SPRING DATE—March 18, 1943. AVERAGE—April 4.

LATEST FALL DATE—November 12, 1947. AVERAGE—September 15.

HABITAT AND DISTRIBUTION — Marshy edges of ponds and streams. Reported from Shaker Lakes, Sherwin Pond, North Chagrin Pond, Rocky River Valley, Mentor Marsh, Akron Lakes. Concentrations of from 40 (April 19, 1947) to 150 (August 17, 1948) have been reported by J. E. Lieftinck at Wingfoot Lake.

NESTING—While we have no definite nesting data, the presence of the bird here regularly throughout the summer suggests it as a possible locally breeding species. Its habit of nesting at times in company with great blue herons in their colonies may account for its nesting having been overlooked here.

NORTHERN YELLOW-CROWNED NIGHT HERON —
Nyctanassa violacea violacea (Linnaeus)

STATUS—Rare and accidental visitor.

An adult bird of this species was reported seen in the Rocky River Valley by M. Owen Davies, August 17, 1945, about one mile north of Little Cedar Point. Two immature birds of this species were reported at Shaker Lakes August 8, 9, 10, 1948, by Richard P. Klein, R. W. Hill and Vera Carrothers; and on August 14, 1948, at the same place by A. B. Williams. The birds remained here until September 9 and were studied closely with binoculars and 20x scope on many evenings by numerous interested observers. It was possible to make detailed comparisons with immature black-crowned night herons present at the same time and place. Two immature birds of this species were also reported at Wingfoot Lake August 14, 1948, by J. E. Lieftinck.

AMERICAN BITTERN—Botaurus lentiginosus (Montagu)

STATUS—Not uncommon migrant; uncommon summer resident.

EARLIEST SPRING DATE—March 20, 1946. AVERAGE—April 13.

LATEST FALL DATE—November 30, 1930. AVERAGE—October 26.

There are records of birds of this species picked up in weakened condition December 5, 1944, and December 6, 1942. An unusual record is that of a bittern caught in a muskrat trap January 6, 1941, and another January 16, 1941, both at Northfield.

HABITAT AND DISTRIBUTION—Frequents marshy edges of ponds and lakes. During migration sometimes appears in unexpected places such as trees on city streets or in suburban back yards.

NESTING—In marshes usually among cattails. July 1, 1838, a number of half grown young seen "at mouth of the Cuyahoga river" (Kirtland 1838:185). Nesting pairs reported over a period of 7 years (1932-1939) in connection with bird population studies made by J. W. Aldrich at Aurora Pond, and by George Bing at Abram's Lake in 1942. May 13, nest, 4 eggs in patch of bulrush in open pasture near Elyria reported by F. M. Phelps. On July 7, 2 young birds were noted at Sherwin Pond.

EASTERN LEAST BITTERN—Ixobrychus exilis exilis (Gmelin)

STATUS—Not uncommon migrant; not uncommon summer resident.

EARLIEST SPRING DATE—April 9 (no year given—Bent 1926:92).
    AVERAGE—May 15.

LATEST FALL DATE—September 19, 1938.

HABITAT AND DISTRIBUTION—Frequents marshy edges of ponds and lakes, where, because of its shy and retiring habits, it is difficult to find. During migration sometimes appears in most unexpected places, as city streets or suburban home grounds. Probably present in most cattail marshes of the region.

NESTING—Listed by John W. Aldrich as breeding at Aurora Pond, and by Vera Carrothers and Arthur B. Williams as breeding at North Chagrin Pond. Nest is a platform of rushes in a cattail clump a few inches above the water. May 21, nest with eggs. June 17, nest, 1 egg; June 23, 3 eggs. June 19, 2 adults feeding young.

Family CICONIIDAE (Storks and Wood Ibises)

WOOD IBIS—Mycteria americana Linnaeus

STATUS—Rare and accidental visitor.

Wheaton (1882:497), discussing the wood ibis, says that Mr. H. E. Chubb of Cleveland writes him that "a young male, which I have in my collection, was shot last spring ten miles west of Cleveland. There were no others with it." The year was probably 1879.

B. P. Bole, Jr. recalls that there was formerly, in his father's collection, a mounted wood ibis collected by J. K. Bole at a point near where Superior Avenue crosses Doan Brook, probably in

September, 1891. He further recalls, in company with his father, who definitely identified it, seeing another of these birds in Gordon Park in July 1914. Although he was only 6 years old at the time, the "big white bird" made a deep impression on him. He recalls his father's excitement, rushing home to get out the big volume of Wilson's "American Ornithology" to compare the bird just seen with the illustration, and with the mounted bird in the collection.

It is of interest that the capture of a wood ibis in Ohio has more recently been reported from Wilmington by Dr. Frank O. Hazard, head of the Department of Biology of Wilmington College, May 5, 1946. This bird was identified by Edward S. Thomas, of the Ohio State Museum, and the skin is now in the museum collection.

Family THRESKIORNITHIDAE (Ibises and Spoonbills)

EASTERN GLOSSY IBIS—Plegadis falcinellus falcinellus (Linnaeus)

STATUS—Rare and accidental visitor.

We have but one record of this southern bird in this region. Wheaton (1882:498) quotes Kirtland, writing in 1850, as follows: " . . . two of these interesting birds, probably a pair, were seen two years since (1848?), near Fairport, Lake County. One of them, a beautiful male, was shot by Mr. Prugen, and forwarded to us. It was duly skinned and mounted, and may now be seen . . . in the cabinet of Nat. Hist. at the Cleve. Med. Coll."

Order ANSERIFORMES

Family ANATIDAE (Swans, Geese, and Ducks)

WHISTLING SWAN—Cygnus columbianus (Ord)

STATUS—Not uncommon migrant.

EARLIEST SPRING DATE—March 9, 1937. AVERAGE—March 21. LATEST —May 24, 1947.

EARLIEST FALL DATE—October 23, 1938. PEAK OF NUMBERS—First two weeks of November. LATEST—January 15, 1940. A few occasionally spend the winter.

Heaviest migration periods are early April and early November. Many more birds are reported in the autumn than in spring. Flocks number from a few individuals to as many as 100, 200, or 400. During the week of November 12, 1947, Mrs. Francis Sherwin and Maude Doolittle estimated 800 swans passed over Waite Hill. The fall migration is practically over by the end of November, but a few stragglers are recorded in December and January.

HABITAT AND DISTRIBUTION—While this largest of the birds of the region is usually seen on Lake Erie, it is also frequently reported from such small inland lakes as the Akron Lakes, Corning Lake, Shaker Lake, North Chagrin Pond and Sherwin Pond. In flight it often forms enormous "V's" in the sky, which are characteristic of its autumn migration.

TRUMPETER SWAN—Cygnus buccinator Richardson

STATUS—Not now present in the region.

The only record of the occurrence in our region of this species is contained in the "Birds of Cedar Point and Vicinity" by Dr. Lynds Jones (1909:120). He says: "The only capture of this species within the area treated was by Mr. L. M. McCormick on April 20, 1891, at Lorain." Wheaton (1882:516) quotes Winslow as saying that this swan "was occasionally taken at Sandusky Bay and other points on the lake shore."

The probability is that this great bird, once near extinction but now becoming established again in the west, was once a more or less regular visitor to Lake Erie and the Cleveland region during migration periods.

UNGAVA CANADA GOOSE—Branta canadensis interior Todd

According to Dr. J. W. Aldrich this is the form of the Canada goose that passes through the Cleveland region in migration.

STATUS—Common migrant; possible rare summer resident.

EARLIEST SPRING DATE—January 11, 1927 (flock of "60 or more"). AVERAGE—March 15. LATEST—May 17, 1947.

EARLIEST FALL DATE—October 11, 1941 and 1942. AVERAGE—October 20. LATEST—December 29, 1945.

Although there are frequent records of flocks of geese moving north in January, it is in late February and early March that the heaviest migration occurs. One of the earliest "signs of spring" is that of the geese flying over in their big "V" formations, honking as they go. The fall migration southwards is not so impressive because the flocks are more scattered then, but it is in mid-November that they are most in evidence. A few stragglers may be seen in December and January.

HABITAT AND DISTRIBUTION—While most frequently seen along the Lake Erie shore, these conspicuous birds may be observed during migration, on the wing, over any part of the region—even downtown Cleveland. They may also be seen on smaller ponds and lakes inland during the migration period.

NESTING—B. P. Bole, Jr. says: "Bred on Bole farm (adjoining Holden Arboretum) in 1944. Nest on small island in pond. Five young raised. Breeding again on small peninsula in same pond May 1948." In the spring of 1949 a pair of Canada geese nested on a small island in the North Chagrin Pond: April 11, 2 eggs; April 14, 4 eggs; April 15, 5 eggs; May 14, all eggs hatched; May 15, young took to the water. The behavior of these birds indicated that they were only semi-wild.

AMERICAN BRANT—Branta bernicla hrota (Muller)

STATUS—Rare and accidental migrant.

We have but two records of this Atlantic coastal species in our region: March 9, 1924, a flock of 36 seen feeding in a wet meadow near Painesville; and March 23, 1930, a flock of 20 seen in the same place (Hadeler 1930).

WHITE-FRONTED GOOSE—Anser albifrons albifrons (Scopoli)

STATUS—Rare and accidental migrant.

We have three records of this species whose usual migration route is west of the Mississippi River. On March 30, 1930, a flock of 42 were seen feeding in a wet meadow near Painesville (Hadeler 1930). More recently, on March 14, 1948, a flock of 5 of these geese were flushed from the Wildfowl Pool at the Cleveland Zoo. They were seen by Robert Mattlin, Paul Schuster and Roland Eschedor, all members of the Zoo staff. Within a few minutes the 5 birds returned, circling low overhead and affording a clear view. On October 26, 1949, a flock of 18 were reported seen by W. E. Scheele in a cornfield in Kirtland Hills Village.

LESSER SNOW GOOSE—Chen hyperborea hyperborea (Pallas)

STATUS—Rare migrant.

ONLY SPRING DATE—February 25, 1943 (One bird reported at Independence by Henry B. Merkle).

EARLIEST FALL DATE—October 22, 1936. LATEST—November 24, 1941.
Autumn records include flocks of 5, 20, 30 and 100.

HABITAT AND DISTRIBUTION — The Lake Erie shore, Beaver Creek, and Corning Lake are the localities within our area from which we have autumn records.

BLUE GOOSE—Chen caerulescens (Linnaeus)

STATUS—Rare migrant.

EARLIEST SPRING DATE—April 21, 1941. LATEST—May 25, 1940.

EARLIEST FALL DATE — October 22, 1936. LATEST — November 25, 1948.

A straggler reported December 8, 1940. Another, an immature bird, was present from November 17 to December 11, 1945, at Lakewood City Park, where it walked about on the lawn eating grass. Seen most frequently and in greatest numbers in late October and early November.

HABITAT AND DISTRIBUTION — The Lake Erie shore and small inland lakes such as Sherwin Pond, Shaker Lake, Mentor Marsh, Clague Pond.

COMMON MALLARD—Anas platyrhynchos platyrhynchos
Linnaeus

STATUS—Common migrant; not uncommon summer resident.

EARLIEST SPRING DATE—March 7, 1926. AVERAGE—March 15.

Due to the fact that a few mallards usually winter here, it is difficult to determine the latest date of true autumn migration. Flocks begin to assemble as early as August 9. The largest flocks occur in November, and have been recorded as late as November 30. If the winter is an open one, numbers of mallards may linger through January.

HABITAT AND DISTRIBUTION — This is a duck of the marshes, small ponds and bogs, and the marshy shores of inland lakes. In migration it may be looked for on almost any body of water.

NESTING—On the ground, usually near water, but sometimes in open fields. April 12, nest, 16 eggs. April 18, nest, 11 eggs. April 28, nest, 13 eggs. May 12, nest, 11 eggs. May 13, nest, 6 eggs. May 25, nest, 10 eggs. Reported breeding at Aurora Pond, Black Brook, Corning Lake, Novelty, Elyria, North Chagrin Pond.

BLACK DUCK—Anas rubripes Brewster

STATUS—Common migrant; not uncommon summer resident.

EARLIEST SPRING DATE—March 3, 1948. AVERAGE—March 13.

Due to the fact that many black ducks usually winter here, it is difficult to determine the latest date of true autumn migration. Flocks begin to assemble as early as August 9. The largest flocks occur in November and December. Many black ducks regularly winter on Lake Erie, where they may be found in flocks numbering hundreds.

In a week by week census of the ducks of the Lake Erie shore from Rocky River to East 140th Street conducted by the Kirtland Bird Club from October 5, 1941, to March 29, 1942, black ducks were found to constitute 14.5 per cent of the wintering duck population, the largest number seen on any one day being 590 on December 7, 1941, and the average for the period being approximately 100.

HABITAT AND DISTRIBUTION—Found along the Lake Erie shore and smaller inland lakes during migration.

NESTING—On the ground near small bogs and ponds, or marshy areas. May 23, nest, 4 eggs. May 31, nest under briars, 9 eggs. June 23, 2 adults and 7 young. Breeding pairs reported at Corning Lake, Aurora Pond, Mentor Marsh, Hinckley Lake, and Wingfoot Lake, Mogadore Reservoir and Summit Lake (near Akron).

GADWALL—Anas strepera Linnaeus

STATUS—Uncommon migrant.

EARLIEST SPRING DATE — March 3, 1945. AVERAGE — March 18. LATEST—May 26, 1946.

EARLIEST FALL DATE — September 20, 1942. LATEST—December 9, 1945.

Single individuals reported January 15, 1940; January 29, February 2, 6, 1945; January 29, 1947; February 2, 1947.

HABITAT AND DISTRIBUTION—Commonly seen on inland ponds or lakes, as well as along the Lake Erie shore. Sometimes turns up in unusual places, as the old Ohio Canal, the Cuyahoga Valley, or in a flooded open field. Usually observed as single individuals or in small flocks of from 2 to 10. There are records in October and November of flocks of 25 and 30.

EUROPEAN WIDGEON—Mareca penelope (Linnaeus)

STATUS—Rare migrant.

This European species has been rather consistently reported in recent years during the migration period, usually, though not always, as single individuals noted among flocks of other species of ducks. It is often associated with the native baldpate.

SPRING DATES—March 7, 1948; March 14, 1919; March 19, 1945; March 20, 1948; March 22, 1944; March 25, 1948; March 28, 1936; March 30, 1947; April 4, 1948; April 5, 1914; April 13, 1941; April 22, 1944; May 22, 1944.

FALL DATES—November 1, 1942; November 7, 1938; November 24, 1941.

HABITAT AND DISTRIBUTION—All records in our region are from Sherwin Pond, Black Brook, Shaker Lakes, Corning Lake, Clague Pond, Long Lake (near Akron), Ravenna. The bird has also been reported from Pymatuning and Sandusky.

BALDPATE—Mareca americana (Gmelin)

STATUS—Common migrant.

EARLIEST SPRING DATE — March 3, 1948. AVERAGE—March 16. LATEST—May 21, 1939 and 1946.

EARLIEST FALL DATE—September 6, 1941. AVERAGE—September 15. LATEST—December 26, 1933 and 1934.

Three unusual records are: Three baldpates reported seen on Sherwin Pond August 10, 1940, and 10 several days later; 12 seen February 28, 1948 on the lakefront. Greatest concentrations of numbers occur in early April and late November.

27

HABITAT AND DISTRIBUTION—Most commonly seen during migration along the Lake Erie shore, but also often in considerable numbers on inland ponds or lakes, such as Sherwin Pond, the Akron Lakes, Black Brook and Shaker Lake.

AMERICAN PINTAIL—Anas acuta tzitzihoa Vieillot

STATUS—Common migrant.

EARLIEST SPRING DATE — March 4, 1939. AVERAGE — March 17. LATEST—May 25, 1921. Heaviest spring migration occurs in March.

EARLIEST FALL DATE—August 26, 1938. Small migrating flocks are not uncommon in October and November. A few individuals may winter along the Lake Erie shore, if the winter is an open one.

HABITAT AND DISTRIBUTION — Recorded from the Lake Erie shore, and during migration from most inland lakes and ponds of the region.

GREEN-WINGED TEAL—Anas carolinensis Gmelin

STATUS—Uncommon migrant.

EARLIEST SPRING DATE — March 6, 1938. AVERAGE—March 15. LATEST—May 30, 1946.

LATEST FALL DATE—November 30, 1941. AVERAGE—November 1.

HABITAT AND DISTRIBUTION—Usually seen in small numbers on small inland ponds and lakes.

BLUE-WINGED TEAL—Anas discors Linnaeus

STATUS—Common migrant; uncommon summer resident.

EARLIEST SPRING DATE—March 6, 1947. AVERAGE—March 29.

LATEST FALL DATE—November 30, 1939.

Usually not seen in large flocks, though there is a record of a flock of 50 seen on Shaker Lake October 4, 1936; and records of flocks of 60 to 100 on the Akron Lakes during fall migration.

HABITAT AND DISTRIBUTION—Usually seen on the smaller inland ponds and lakes during migration seasons.

NESTING—One pair reported by John W. Aldrich as nesting at Aurora Pond 1932-34, and again 1936-39. The probability is that this species nests in other favorable localities within our region. Nests have been reported for nearby areas.

SHOVELLER—Spatula clypeata (Linnaeus)

STATUS—Uncommon migrant.

EARLIEST SPRING DATE — March 6, 1949. AVERAGE — March 21. LATEST—April 30, 1947.

EARLIEST FALL DATE—September 4, 1948. AVERAGE—October 8. LATEST—December 27, 1941.

There is also a record of 7 seen February 25, 1945, which may be considered either as a wintering record or an unusually early spring migration record. Unusual records are 1 bird seen August 24, 1945, and another August 14, 1938.

HABITAT AND DISTRIBUTION—Commonly frequents the Lake Erie shore or interior small ponds or lakes during migration. Usually seen as single individuals or in small flocks of 3 to 11. One record of a flock of 24, December 17, 1939.

WOOD DUCK—Aix sponsa (Linnaeus)

STATUS—Common migrant; not uncommon summer resident.

EARLIEST SPRING DATE—February 28, 1948. AVERAGE—March 16.

LATEST FALL DATE—November 30, 1939. AVERAGE—November 13.

PEAK OF NUMBERS—Late October.

Unusual records are: 4 seen at Aurora Pond December 9, 1945; a female on Clague Pond December 29, 1946, January 18 and 26, 1947; and 1 bird at Cleveland December 22, 1927 (specimen).

HABITAT AND DISTRIBUTION—Frequents small ponds, bogs and quiet stretches of rivers. Seen on most inland lakes during migration, when, in the autumn especially, it gathers into small flocks (25-50). Has been reported in summer from such places as Corning Lake, Aurora Pond, Mentor Marsh, Brecksville (Cuyahoga River and Canal), Hinckley Lake, North Chagrin, Sherwin Pond.

NESTING—In holes in trees, often at quite a distance from the ground or from water. Nesting begins first week in May. Young are out of the nest by mid-June. May 18, female entering nest hole in large sycamore in Rocky River Valley about 50 feet from ground. May 31, Aurora Pond, adults with at least 6 young. June 1, female in old pileated woodpecker hole. July 4, female followed by 8 small young at Hinckley Lake.

REDHEAD—Aythya americana (Eyton)

STATUS—Uncommon migrant; uncommon winter visitor.

EARLIEST SPRING DATE — March 1, 1946. AVERAGE — March 20. LATEST—April 27, 1947.

EARLIEST FALL DATE—October 29, 1948. AVERAGE—November 20. LATEST—December 31, 1947.

It is difficult if not impossible to separate the latest recorded wintering dates from the first truly migratory dates in February and March. If the winter is an open one, many redheads undoubtedly stay over on the lake, and merge with the migrating flocks later. Those seen during January and February on Lake Erie are usually a few individuals only, although occasionally large flocks (400-1000-1600) have been reported in January. A report of 75 on March 1, 1946, looks like real migration.

HABITAT AND DISTRIBUTION—Commonly seen on Lake Erie and during migration on smaller inland lakes and ponds.

RING-NECKED DUCK—Aythya collaris (Donovan)

STATUS—Not uncommon migrant; not uncommon winter visitor.

EARLIEST SPRING DATE — March 1, 1948. AVERAGE — March 18. LATEST—May 15, 1938.

EARLIEST FALL DATE — October 4, 1941. AVERAGE — October 14. LATEST—December 27, 1941. Occasional individuals recorded in January and February.

Most abundant during the migratory flights of November and March. Often seen with other ducks, particularly lesser scaups.

HABITAT AND DISTRIBUTION—Lake Erie and smaller inland lakes and ponds during migration.

CANVASBACK—Aythya valisineria (Wilson)

STATUS—Uncommon migrant; uncommon winter visitor.

EARLIEST SPRING DATE—March 2, 1946. LATEST—May 11, 1947.

EARLIEST FALL DATE—September 18, 1948. LATEST—December 26, 1945 and 1948. A few winter here if the weather is not too severe.

This duck seems to have been seldom recorded in our region in numbers greater than single birds, or at most, a few individuals at a time, except for a record of a flock of 200, April 5, 1931, and another of 200 December 26, 1948. Apparently our birds are on the fringes of the flocks that annually pass through the Sandusky marshes to the west, and Pymatuning Reservoir to the east. Under these circumstances it is difficult to set ''early'' and ''last'' dates.

HABITAT AND DISTRIBUTION—Reported usually from the Lake Erie shore, although occasionally also from inland lakes or ponds.

GREATER SCAUP DUCK—Aythya marila nearctica Stejneger

STATUS—Uncommon migrant; uncommon winter visitor.

EARLIEST SPRING DATE—March 7, 1947. LATEST—May 13, 1947.

ONLY FALL DATES—November 3, 1946; November 28, 1943.

There are a few wintering dates: January 18, 1942; January 21, 1940; February 17, 1934 (specimen collected) (Trautman 1935:202); February 22, 1940. An unusual winter record is the following for 1948: January 3, flock of 6 reported by J. E. Lieftinck, and on January 31 a flock of 400 by the same observer. On February 1 a flock of 10, and on February 7 a flock of 100 were reported by Margarette E. Morse. On February 14 James S. Findley reported 100 and on February 21 Morse reported 10.

The fact that it is difficult to separate this species from the lesser scaup unless seen in company with that species, is no doubt responsible for the few records of occurrence which we have. As a matter of fact, the bird may not be so rare as we think it is. Our records, however, do not agree with Peterson's statement (1947:46) that the greater scaup is the ''winter Scaup of the Great Lakes.''

HABITAT AND DISTRIBUTION — Records of localities are Lake Erie, Shaker Lake, Wade Park Pond, Mentor Marsh.

LESSER SCAUP DUCK—Aythya affinis (Eyton)

STATUS—Abundant migrant; common winter visitor.

EARLIEST FALL DATE — October 6, 1945. AVERAGE — October 17. Many individuals customarily spend the winter on Lake Erie.

EARLIEST SPRING DATE—March 1, 1948. PEAK OF NUMBERS—About May 12-18. LATEST—May 30, 1935, 1937, 1946, 1947.

This is easily our most abundant duck, both during migration and throughout the winter. Its flocks, riding the waves behind the breakwater, or even far out in the lake, are often estimated in the thousands. Flocks decrease in numbers toward February.

In a week by week census of the ducks of the Lake Erie shore from Rocky River to East 140th Street conducted by the Kirtland Bird Club from October 5, 1941 to March 29, 1942, lesser scaups were found to constitute 86.18 per cent of total ducks observed, and 28.08 per cent of the wintering duck population. Numbers varied from 0 to 10,838, the average being 2,502.

HABITAT AND DISTRIBUTION — From October to March these hardy ducks are a familiar sight along the lake shore wherever there is open water. During migration they also appear on inland lakes and ponds in numbers. In spring they appear as soon as the ice breaks up.

AMERICAN GOLDENEYE—Bucephala clangula americana (Bonaparte)

STATUS—Common migrant; common winter visitor.

EARLIEST SPRING DATE—March 1, 1942 and 1948. AVERAGE—April 18. LATEST—May 22, 1947.

EARLIEST FALL DATE—September 14, 1941. AVERAGE—September 20. LATEST — December 27, 1926 and 1941. A few regularly spend the winter.

The period of greatest abundance for this species is during December, when small flocks are regularly seen along the lakefront.

In a week by week census of the ducks along the Lake Erie shore from Rocky River to East 140th Street conducted by the

32

Kirtland Bird Club from October 5, 1941 to March 29, 1942, American goldeneyes were found to constitute 1.61 per cent of all ducks observed, and 2.17 per cent of the wintering flocks. Numbers varied from 0 to 166, the average being 47.

HABITAT AND DISTRIBUTION — Seen most frequently on Lake Erie, but also commonly on smaller inland ponds and lakes as well as the larger streams. A few frequently winter on Fairmount Reservoir.

BARROW'S GOLDENEYE—Bucephala islandica (Gmelin)

STATUS—Rare and accidental visitor.

Lynds Jones (1909:117) says: "There is the skin of a female (of this species) in the Oberlin College collection which was captured on April 5, 1892, at Lorain, by Mr. Harry Warden." A male was shot by Harlan Sherman of Willoughby in a lagoon back of Richmond Beach and identified by F. N. Shankland, December 17, 1923; December 18, 1923, a male was shot at the same place by another hunter, also identified by Shankland.

BUFFLEHEAD—Bucephala albeola (Linnaeus)

STATUS—Not uncommon migrant; not uncommon winter visitor.

EARLIEST SPRING DATE — March 2, 1925. AVERAGE — March 16. LATEST—May 18, 1947. An unusual record of 3 seen with some mallards at Hinckley Lake June 1, 1941.

EARLIEST FALL DATE — October 14, 1941. AVERAGE — October 19. LATEST—December 31, 1933. A few may spend the winter.

Most numerous in November and April. Usually seen in small numbers (1-6), occasionally in small flocks (14-25).

HABITAT AND DISTRIBUTION—The Lake Erie shore and smaller inland lakes and ponds during migration.

OLDSQUAW—Clangula hyemalis (Linnaeus)

STATUS—Uncommon migrant; uncommon winter visitor.

EARLIEST SPRING DATE—March 1, 1948. LATEST—April 23, 1947. Two reports of stragglers: May 6, 1944, male in summer plumage, Lake Erie at Gordon Park; May 15, 1927, "young male", Lake Erie at Fairport.

EARLIEST FALL DATE — October 12, 1941. Most records are of December and January occurrences—usually of single birds or not more than 2 together (one record of 6 at Akron Lakes April 20, 1947). A few sometimes spend the winter, as appears below.

HABITAT AND DISTRIBUTION — Records are from the Lake Erie shore, Cuyahoga Falls, the Akron Lakes, and Fairmount Reservoir. A constant flow of water in the reservoir usually keeps a small area of open water even in severe winter weather. Two old-squaws were observed here frequently during January and February of 1944, as well as another here February 22, 1936.

AMERICAN EIDER—Somateria mollissima Sharpe

STATUS—Rare and accidental winter visitor.

The only record of this species in our region is that of one female seen December 7, 1947, at Edgewater Park, by R. W. Hill, Margaret Cook and Bob Foley; and reported at the same place December 13, 1947 by M. Owen Davies and Fred J. Ackerman; and December 14, 1947 by Vera Carrothers. Identification as between this species and *S. spectabilis* determined on the basis of careful study of bill characters. Identification made at close quarters with binoculars and ''spotoscope''.

KING EIDER—Somateria spectabilis (Linnaeus)

STATUS—Rare and accidental winter visitor.

Wheaton (1882:536) speaks of a specimen reported by Winslow collected ''many years since'' at Cleveland. One was reported seen in the midst of a flock of Bonaparte's gulls at White City November 18, 1945, by R. W. Hill and George King. One reported 6 times in December 1947, twice in January 1948, and 3 times in February 1948 (possibly the same bird) at Clifton Beach, Edgewater Park, and Gordon Park, by various observers (10 in all). Two spring records are: March 20, 1948, and April 20, 1947, both from Lake Dorothy, reported by J. E. Lieftinck.

WHITE-WINGED SCOTER—Melanitta deglandi (Bonaparte)

STATUS—Uncommon migrant; uncommon winter visitor.

EARLIEST SPRING DATE — March 1, 1946. AVERAGE — March 7. LATEST—(unusually late) May 25, 1938, reported by Mitchell at Cuyahoga Falls (Walker 1938b:290).

EARLIEST FALL DATE—September 2, 1944. AVERAGE—November 3. LATEST — November 22, 1942. A few occasionally spend the winter. A female wintered with a small flock of goldeneyes on Fairmount Reservoir December 19, 1943 to February 22, 1944 (Findley).

Most commonly reported in December and January, decreasing in numbers in February. Usually seen as single individuals or in small groups (2-6).

HABITAT AND DISTRIBUTION—Usually seen on Lake Erie, though there is a record for Cuyahoga Falls and one for Fairmount Reservoir (see above).

SURF SCOTER—Melanitta perspicillata (Linnaeus)

STATUS—Rare and occasional fall and winter visitor.

The only records for this species, seldom reported in our region, are the following: October 19, 1919, one juvenile seen at Fairport by Doolittle (1920a:66). January 19, 1930, one seen at Gordon Park by W. H. Watterson. October 17, 1931, one collected by D. F. Wallace at Richmond Beach (skin in CMNH collection). December 21, 1941, one seen at Cleveland by R. W. Hill, James F. Akers and Don Eckelberry. November 10, 1945, 7 reported seen by R. W. Hill at Richmond Beach. January 18, 1947, one seen at Richmond Beach by R. W. Hill. January 3, 1948, one reported at Cleveland lakefront by James S. Findley, J. E. Lieftinck, Jerry Piskac, Ray Smiley.

HABITAT AND DISTRIBUTION — All records thus far have been made either along the Lake Erie shore or in waters immediately adjoining the lake.

AMERICAN SCOTER—Oidemia nigra americana Swainson

STATUS—Rare and occasional migrant.

The only records we have for the region are the following: April 7, 1940, 2 seen at Edgewater Park by J. O. McQuown. April 18, 1937, 3 seen on Hinckley Lake by F. D. Johnson and Arthur B. Williams. April 26, 1936, 1 seen at Gordon Park by B. P. Bole, Jr. November 2, 1941, 2 females seen together at White City by J. W. Aldrich, Vera Carrothers, Margarette E. Morse,

Marjorie Ramisch. November 4, 1917, 1 male seen at Fairport by E. A. Doolittle (1920a:66). November 4, 1945, 3 seen at White City by W. Earl Godfrey. December 27, 1937, January 2, 1938, 1 reported at Fairport by James F. Akers. January 3, 4, 5, 6, 1948, 1 reported at Cleveland lakefront by Vera Carrothers, James S. Findley, J. E. Lieftinck.

HABITAT AND DISTRIBUTION—All records except one (Hinckley Lake) are for the Lake Erie shore.

RUDDY DUCK—Oxyura jamaicensis rubida (Wilson)

STATUS—Not uncommon migrant.

EARLIEST SPRING DATE — March 3, 1946. AVERAGE — March 23. PEAK OF NUMBERS—April. LATEST—June 10, 1943.

EARLIEST FALL DATE — October 4, 1936. AVERAGE — October 18. LATEST—January 11, 1948. Occasionally individuals will winter.

Heaviest autumn migration late October and early November. While usually seen in small numbers, sometimes migrating flocks will number 150 to 500 birds.

HABITAT AND DISTRIBUTION—The Lake Erie shore and smaller inland lakes and ponds throughout the region.

HOODED MERGANSER—Lophodytes cucullatus (Linnaeus)

STATUS—Not uncommon migrant.

EARLIEST SPRING DATE—March 2, 1941 and 1947. AVERAGE—March 15. LATEST—May 29, 1938.

EARLIEST FALL DATE—September 10, 1940. AVERAGE—October 18. LATEST—January 30, 1938.

Heaviest migration periods are in March and November. A few may spend the winter.

HABITAT AND DISTRIBUTION—Unlike the two following species, which are observed most frequently along the Lake Erie shore, this small merganser is more commonly found during the migration period on small inland lakes, ponds and streams. Two pairs were even reported seen on a small pond on a golf course March 20, 1940.

AMERICAN MERGANSER—Mergus merganser americanus Cassin

STATUS—Common migrant; common winter visitor.

EARLIEST SPRING DATE — March 3, 1948. AVERAGE — April 18. LATEST—May 18, 1946.

EARLIEST FALL DATE—September 25, 1943. AVERAGE—October 21.

Often seen in large numbers, flocks of 1200 and 1600 having been reported. Most numerous in November and December. This species is mentioned among the birds common to the Cleveland region "at the time of the first surveys" (1796) (Kirtland 1850).

In a week by week study of wintering ducks along the Lake Erie shore from the mouth of Rocky River to East 140th Street conducted by members of the Kirtland Bird Club from October 5, 1941 to March 29, 1942, American mergansers were found to constitute 5.29 per cent of all ducks observed, and 44.0 per cent of the wintering flocks. Numbers varied from 5 to 845, the average being 172.

HABITAT AND DISTRIBUTION—While this species is most commonly observed along the Lake Erie shore it sometimes appears on such inland waters as Sherwin Pond, Hinckley Lake and the Akron Lakes.

RED-BREASTED MERGANSER—Mergus serrator serrator Linnaeus

STATUS—Common migrant; common winter visitor.

EARLIEST SPRING DATE—March 3, 1948. AVERAGE—April 20. Many May dates. LATEST—June 3, 1939.

EARLIEST FALL DATE — October 3, 1942. AVERAGE — October 12. LATEST—January 25, 1931.

Most numerous in November and December, when flocks of 100 or more may often be seen along the Lake Erie shore. Heaviest migration in April and November. Often winters on Lake Erie.

During a week by week census of the ducks of the Lake Erie shore from Rocky River to East 140th Street conducted by the Kirtland Bird Club from October 5, 1941 to March 29, 1942, red-breasted mergansers were found to constitute 2.24 per cent of all ducks observed, and 10.39 per cent of the wintering flocks. Numbers varied from 20 to 166, the average being 65.

HABITAT AND DISTRIBUTION—While most frequently seen along the Lake Erie shore, this species is not an uncommon bird during the migration period on small inland lakes, ponds and the larger streams.

Order FALCONIFORMES

Family CATHARTIDAE (American Vultures)

EASTERN TURKEY VULTURE—Cathartes aura septentrionalis Wied.

STATUS—Common migrant; uncommon summer resident.

EARLIEST SPRING DATE—February 3, 1939. PEAK OF NUMBERS—March 20 through April (Hinckley Lake).

LATEST FALL DATE—December 22, 1928.

Height of abundance is reached in March and again in October.

HABITAT AND DISTRIBUTION—Occurs most commonly throughout the open farmlands of the area. It may often be seen over woodlands and river valleys. Well distributed throughout the area. Nearly always to be seen in numbers in spring about Hinckley Lake. Kirkpatrick (1859:343) says: "Prior to 1832-4 (turkey buzzards) were very numerous around Cleveland. A favorite roosting place was in the immediate vicinity of where the Medical College now stands" (corner of Central Avenue and East 14th Street).

NESTING—On the ground in hollow logs in woodlands, or in caves along waterways when sections of the bedrock have been exposed. 1893, nest on Gildersleeve Mountain (a conglomerate ledge of 1160 feet elevation in Kirtland Township, Lake County) on ground at bottom of crevasse in conglomerate ledges, 2 eggs (Shankland). April 28, 1946, 2 eggs in hollow stump. May 5, 1940, nest. B. P. Bole, Jr. reports one nesting pair on Little Mountain from 1932 to 1938 inclusive. June 3, 1948, Hinckley Lake, nest in hollow log with 3 well incubated eggs; June 13, eggs still unhatched. August 2, 1949, near Gates Mills, nest 10 feet inside hollow log in woods, 1 young bird fully feathered.

38

Family ACCIPITRIIDAE (Kites, Hawks, and Allies)

SWALLOW-TAILED KITE—Elanoides forficatus forficatus (Linnaeus)

STATUS—Not now present in the region.

This species was mentioned by Kirtland (1850) as among the birds common to the region at the time of "the first surveys" (1796). Dr. Kirtland (1838:178) wrote: "A few years since the swallow-tailed hawk was to be seen during the summer, in considerable numbers in Portage and Stark Counties. From some unknown cause it has, of late, ceased to visit these localities." Kirkpatrick (1859:360-361) says: "This beautiful bird was once pretty plentiful in Ohio, and often seen in Summit and Portage counties . . . Very fine specimen in the cabinet of Prof. Kirtland."

At present this species occurs chiefly in South Carolina, Florida and Louisiana.

EASTERN GOSHAWK—Accipiter gentilis atricapillus (Wilson)

STATUS—Rare and occasional visitor.

Kirkpatrick (1858a) mentions a goshawk shot near Cleveland. More recent records are: November 14, 1928 at Hudson, collected by Fred Glenny; August 7, 1933, one collected at Gates Mills by John P. Sawyer; October 2, 1941, one seen by Rudolph J. Kula at Auburn Center; November 24, 30, and December 9, 1941, at Willow (probably same bird, observed by Raymond Roth attacking ring-necked pheasants); January 10, 1947, one seen at North Chagrin by M. B. Walters.

HABITAT AND DISTRIBUTION—Typically a bird of the northern coniferous forests, it might appear almost anywhere here.

NESTING—There is a record of an egg of this species having been collected "near Cleveland" by R. K. Winslow (Brewer 1859:18,131).

SHARP-SHINNED HAWK—Accipiter striatus velox (Wilson)

STATUS—Uncommon migrant; uncommon permanent resident.

Most frequently observed during migration in April and May. Thirty sharp-shins were identified as part of an impressive hawk flight May 5, 1946, proceeding easterly over Bay Village.

39

HABITAT AND DISTRIBUTION — A forest and forest-edge bird, rarely seen in other habitats. Occurs sparingly throughout the region in such habitats, and is occasionally seen in suburban areas.

NESTING—There are 4 records of the nesting of this bird in the Cleveland region. F. N. Shankland describes a nest of the sharp-shin as found May 16, 1934, by himself and Hugh Bell. Located in Joplin's Woods, Willoughby, in a tall, slim hemlock, standing at the brow of a steep wooded hillside. The nest was in an old crow's nest. The hawks had made a rough cup-like depression on one side of the original nest, slightly larger than a robin's nest. There were 5 eggs.

One pair was recorded by B. P. Bole, Jr., as nesting on Little Mountain in 1938.

Another record is from North Chagrin. This nest was discovered at a height of 30 feet in a 12-inch hemlock, and appeared to be composed entirely of dead hemlock twigs. On July 12, 1947, four young birds, three of which were ready to fly, were taken from the nest. Eggs were probably laid the last week in May.

At Aurora May 16, 21, 1949, nest built of sticks on remains of green heron nest 13 feet up in wild apple thicket, 3 eggs; June 6, female incubating 4 eggs; June 20, 4 downy young with eyes open; July 3, 3 young visible over rim of nest; July 8, 3 young three-quarters grown; July 9, 3 young on edge of nest; July 15, 1 young in nest (Carl F. Hamann).

COOPER'S HAWK—Accipiter cooperii (Bonaparte)

STATUS—Common migrant; common permanent resident.

On May 5, 1946, at Bay Village, 65 Cooper's hawks were identified as a part of an impressive flight of hawks proceeding easterly on that day.

HABITAT AND DISTRIBUTION — A forest and forest-edge bird, rarely being found far from woods. Widely distributed in the region, and even occurring in wooded portions of the suburbs of Cleveland.

NESTING—In forest trees, generally at heights of 30 to 50 feet or more from the ground. April 18, bird repairing old nest; May 4, bird flushed from nest. April 21, female flew from nest; April 28, male scolding and female again flew from nest. May 3, nest. May 12, nest. May 29, adult on nest. June 10, nest with young;

40

June 18, young still in nest; June 21, 3 young visible; June 29, 2 young visible. April 22, 29, May 6, female on nest; May 19, 20, birds absent; May 28, 29, female on nest; June 26, 3 full grown nestlings, 1 left nest; July 22, nest empty. July 8, 11, three downy young in nest.

EASTERN RED-TAILED HAWK—Buteo jamaicensis borealis (Gmelin)

STATUS—Common migrant; common permanent resident. Numbers reduced during winter.

HABITAT AND DISTRIBUTION—In this region the red-tailed hawk is a bird of the woodlands, though it is often to be seen over the adjacent fields and farmlands. Widely distributed throughout the region in suitable habitats, seeming often to prefer wooded river valleys.

NESTING—In forest trees, usually at heights of fifty feet or above. The same nest may be used year after year. The nest is fairly large, constructed of twigs and sticks. Among many nesting records, the following are typical: March 15, bird near old nest; March 30, bird on nest; April 26, bird on nest; May 16, nest empty. April 3, 10, eggs in nest. April 16, bird on nest; April 20, 2 downy young; May 18, young almost full grown. April 30, nesting; May 14, 2 young in downy stage. May 19, nest with small downy young. May 23, bird on nest. May 23, 2 young left nest. August 8, 1 adult, 2 young on wing.

NORTHERN RED-SHOULDERED HAWK—Buteo lineatus lineatus (Gmelin)

STATUS—Common migrant; common permanent resident. Numbers reduced during winter.

Our most common large hawk. Fifteen red-shouldered hawks were identified as part of an impressive hawk flight May 5, 1946, at Bay Village.

HABITAT AND DISTRIBUTION—Prefers the vicinity of wooded areas and adjacent fields. Commonly observed in river valleys and woodlands of the region.

NESTING—In forest trees usually at heights of 35 feet or more. March 31, nest nearly completed. March 31, bird on nest in sycamore; April 28, 2 young in nest; June 8, nest empty. April 6, bird flushed from nest. May 4, bird on nest. May 11, bird on nest. May 21, bird on nest; June 16, 2 young out of nest. May 30, nest in beech, 2 young about 3 weeks old. June 29, one young leaving nest. July 9, 2 young taken from nest. Records of 4 nests with eggs are as follows: April 6, 4 eggs. April 22, 4 eggs. April 24, 2 eggs. May 4, 2 eggs.

BROAD-WINGED HAWK—Buteo platypterus platypterus (Vieillot)

STATUS—Not uncommon migrant; uncommon summer resident.

Kirtland (1850) mentions it as among the birds common to Cleveland at the time of the first surveys (1796).

EARLIEST SPRING DATE—February 11, 1948. Largest flights of migrating birds have been recorded from the 24th to the 29th of April. There are very few summer and fall records.

ONLY FALL DATES—October 16, 1946, and October 30, 1943.

Apparently one bird wintered in the vicinity of Wickliffe 1939-40 (R. W. Hill, A. B. Fuller); and another was reported seen at Forest Hill, East Cleveland, several times from December 22, 1947, to January 25, 1948, by George King.

HABITAT AND DISTRIBUTION—Observed usually in open places not far from trees, often in the larger river valleys. On migration they fly high, progressing in great loops and circles.

NESTING—Usually in forest trees. A pair was reported by B. P. Bole, Jr., as nesting on Little Mountain in 1938. J. E. Lieftinck reports a nest in the Akron Metropolitan Park with the bird on the nest May 31 and June 15, 1947.

AMERICAN ROUGH-LEGGED HAWK—Buteo lagopus s. johannis (Gmelin)

STATUS—Uncommon migrant; uncommon winter visitor.

EARLIEST FALL DATE—September 20, 1941. PEAK OF NUMBERS—November. Usually present in small numbers throughout the winter.

LATEST SPRING DATE—May 16, 1943.

Doolittle (1919b) records a migrating flock of 20 at Painesville on April 27, 1919. During some winters they appear to be relatively common, while during others they are almost absent. During the winter of 1858-9 they were reported to have been particularly numerous (Wheaton 1882:431).

HABITAT AND DISTRIBUTION—Appears to prefer stretches of open fields where it is often observed perched in low trees. Here it has been recorded most commonly at various places along the Lake Erie shore, in the Rocky River Valley, and in the large open areas throughout the region.

GOLDEN EAGLE—Aquila chrysaëtos canadensis (Linnaeus)

STATUS—Rare or accidental migrant.

Mentioned by Kirtland (1850) as among the birds common to Cleveland at the time of the first surveys (1796). Kirtland (1874b:209) also says it was occasionally seen flying along the lake shore in 1810. Dawson (1903:413) reports seeing one on the Lake Erie shore near Lorain, August 29, 1898. F. N. Shankland reports one collected November 16, 1901, in the Chagrin Valley, by Elmer Jenkins, taxidermist, of Willoughby, and mounted by him. A more recent record is one reported seen twice, soaring overhead, by B. P. Bole, Jr., and others, at the Holden Arboretum May 28, 1940.

NORTHERN BALD EAGLE—Haliaeetus leucocephalus washingtonii (Audubon)

STATUS—Rare permanent resident.

Formerly nested regularly in the region, but there are few nesting records in recent years. James Smith (1907:26) while a captive of the Indians (1755 to 1759) noted "numbers of Bald and Gray Eagles" near the mouth of the Black River (Lorain).

HABITAT AND DISTRIBUTION—Although so large a bird as the eagle is rarely restricted in habitat, it may be said that in this region this bird has most often been seen near the lakefront, in the large river valleys, and somewhat less commonly near inland lakes.

NESTING—The bald eagle once nested on the Kirtland estate at Rockport (now Lakewood), and there are a number of references in the literature to this pair. Kirtland reported that he carefully observed this pair from about 1845-1858 (Wheaton 1882:435,436).

Dr. Ralph W. Dexter, of Kent State University, says that about 1935 a pair nested at Lake Rockwell.

The chief breeding grounds of the bald eagle in northern Ohio are now the Lake Erie islands and the shores about the western end of the lake.

AMERICAN MARSH HAWK—Circus cyaneus hudsonius (Linnaeus)

STATUS—Common migrant; common permanent resident. Numbers reduced during winter.

HABITAT AND DISTRIBUTION—A bird of the open fields and marshes. Generally distributed throughout the region in such habitats.

NESTING—On the ground in open fields or marshy areas. The nest is constructed of rushes and grasses. March 22, male in courtship flight. April 20, male in courtship flight. May 10, 5 eggs. May 16, 6 eggs. May 16, 5 eggs. May 29, eggs. June 28, 4 eggs. A quite complete record of a nest at Aurora Sanctuary was made by Harry E. Duer as follows: May 7, 1 egg; May 14, 4 eggs; May 21, 5 eggs; May 30, 5 eggs; June 4, 5 eggs; June 11, 3 eggs, 2 young; June 17, 5 young; July 16, all young left nest. An unusual record is that of a nest near Willoughby containing 8 eggs on April 28.

Family PANDIONIDAE (Ospreys)

AMERICAN OSPREY—Pandion haliaetus carolinensis (Gmelin)

STATUS—Uncommon to rare migrant.

EARLIEST SPRING DATE — March 25, 1939. AVERAGE — April 27. LATEST—May 28, 1938.

LATEST FALL DATE—October 26, 1942 and 1946. AVERAGE—October 19.

Records on June 17, July 4, and August 8, 12, 16, 22 may indicate possible nearby breeding grounds. Seen most frequently in April, May, and October.

HABITAT AND DISTRIBUTION—Prefers lake shore, inland ponds and river valleys, and is to be looked for in such places in the region.

Family FALCONIDAE (Caracaras and Falcons)

DUCK HAWK—Falco peregrinus anatum Bonaparte

STATUS—Rare migrant.

EARLIEST SPRING DATE—March 6, 1948. LATEST—May 29, 1923.

EARLIEST FALL DATE—August 21, 1945. LATEST—November 30, 1948.

Seen most frequently in May, September and October. There are 2 winter records: January 25, 1947, and January 27, 1931.

HABITAT AND DISTRIBUTION—Unrestricted as to habitat in this region. Has been seen on the lake shore and even in the midst of the City of Cleveland, where one was observed August 21, 1945, on the roof of the Midland Building, eating a green heron.

EASTERN PIGEON HAWK—Falco columbarius columbarius Linnaeus

STATUS—Rare migrant; possible rare summer resident.

SPRING DATES—Most records are for March, April and May, with a concentration of numbers about the middle of May.

FALL AND WINTER DATES—September 20, 1947; November 1, 1938; December 8, 1947; December 23, 1931; January 1, 1947; January 18, 1945.

HABITAT AND DISTRIBUTION—Usually seen in open country, often along the lake shore.

NESTING—Kirtland (1874b:239) reported a pair nesting "for several years" near his home in Rockport (now Lakewood) prior to 1858. Two juveniles were collected. Kendeigh (1924:268) reported a pair breeding "near Cleveland" in the spring of 1924, with the remark that they had been nesting there "for the last year or two."

EASTERN SPARROW HAWK—Falco sparverius sparverius Linnaeus

STATUS—Common migrant; common permanent resident. Numbers reduced during winter.

HABITAT AND DISTRIBUTION—Occurs almost anywhere with the possible exception of the deep woods. Often observed in the midst of the City of Cleveland. More characteristically on wires and fences bordering open fields. Generally distributed throughout the region.

NESTING—In natural tree hollows or old flicker holes or under eaves of buildings from 10 to 40 feet up. April 9, nest, 3 eggs. April 26, nest with 4 eggs; April 27, 5 eggs; May 25, eggs hatched; June 25, 3 young left nest. June 18, young in nest. May 5 (2 nests in hollow limbs of oak trees), bird incubating eggs; July 4, young leave nest.

Order GALLIFORMES

Family TETRAONIDAE (Grouse and Ptarmigans)

APPALACHIAN RUFFED GROUSE—Bonasa umbellus monticola Todd

STATUS—Uncommon permanent resident.

Formerly common, now greatly decreased in numbers in the region.

HABITAT AND DISTRIBUTION—This is a woodland bird, dependent on the continued existence of forested areas of some considerable extent. Now found principally in the Metropolitan Park Reservations east and south of Cleveland, Little Mountain, and in the wooded sections of the Chagrin River drainage system. It sometimes appears in unexpected places, such as suburban sections.

NESTING—Nest on ground, usually at base of tree, bush or stump. Eggs, April 28 to June 10. Adults with young June 3 to August 28. April 28, nest with 13 eggs. May 5, nest, 12 eggs. May 13, bird flushed from nest containing 10 eggs. June 10, nest, 5 eggs.

Family PHASIANIDAE (Quails, Partridges, and Pheasants)

EASTERN BOBWHITE—Colinus virginianus virginianus (Linnaeus)

STATUS—Uncommon permanent resident.

Kirtland (1850), describing the birds of the Cleveland region prior to the first surveys (1796), says, "Quail . . . were not so very abundant."

Numbers are subject to violent fluctuations at times, caused usually by hard winters, when many bobwhites are unable to survive.

HABITAT AND DISTRIBUTION—This is usually a bird of the fields and hedgerows, though frequently it will make itself at home about houses in suburban residence communities, especially if food is provided in winter.

NESTING—Nest on the ground well screened by brambles, fence rails or other protective cover. April 27, ten chicks too young to fly. May 12, nest, 11 eggs. May 12, nest, 12 eggs. July 5, 12 eggs. August 2, male sitting on 11 eggs in nest.

RING-NECKED PHEASANT—Phasianus colchicus Linnaeus

STATUS—Common permanent resident.

The first ring-necked pheasants to be established in the United States were imported from China to Oregon in 1881. In Ohio the bird has only become well established since 1913. The Cleveland region is not good "pheasant country", and the bird can never become so abundant here as in the prairie states.

HABITAT AND DISTRIBUTION—Open country, farmlands, scrubby fields and swampy areas are the chosen haunts of this species. The western part of our region is better adapted to its needs than is the eastern part.

NESTING—Nest on the ground, usually in dense cover in open field, or along fence rows or overgrown country roadsides. Eggs, April 29 to June 25. Young, July 15. Records from Rocky River, Avon, Maple Heights, and East Claridon.

Family MELEAGRIDIDAE (Turkeys)

EASTERN TURKEY—Meleagris gallopavo silvestris Vieillot

STATUS—Formerly a common bird of the region, now no longer found here.

James Smith (1907:27,31), who was captured by the Indians in 1755, was taken by them to the mouth of the Black River (Lorain). He noted that, along the river, turkeys were plentiful. The Indians also had a camp on Rocky River, where again Smith mentions turkeys among the game killed.

The turkey was mentioned by Kirtland (1850) as one of the birds common to the region at the time of the "first surveys" (1796), but in 1864 he noted that only a few were remaining at Rockport (now Lakewood), though still offered for sale in the Cleveland markets (Christy 1936:84).

The diary of Oliver Hazard Perry (1899:97) details some of his hunting trips about Parma and in nearby Lorain and Henry Counties in 1847. Killing a wild turkey was then a common experience.

The cut of the mounted turkey cock appearing as a frontispiece to this volume shows a bird that was in all probability shot within thirty miles of Cleveland. It was mounted by Rufus K. Winslow about 1840, and was no doubt bagged by that zealous collector of birds. It is posed in the attitude shown in the first, and most famous, plate of Audubon's "Birds of America". It formerly stood in the dining room of Mr. Winslow's residence on Euclid Avenue (Memo of Mrs. A. Hall, in files of Western Reserve University).

Order GRUIFORMES

Family GRUIDAE (Cranes)

SANDHILL CRANE—Grus canadensis tabida (Peters)

STATUS—Rare and accidental migrant.

There are several records of this now locally rare bird in our region. J. M. Keck, a cooperator of the U. S. Biological Survey (now Fish and Wildlife Service), reported the bird at Chardon "first seen May 10, 1888, last seen November 7, 1888." Also in the files of the Fish and Wildlife Service is a report by Mrs. F. A. Pritchard of Medina, who states, "Last seen November 8, 1920, 1 or 2." One was reported seen near Richmond April 7, 1946, by F. J. Ackermann, M. Owen Davies, Florence Gray, and Marian Schutler. At Plymouth Marsh, Ashtabula County, just outside our region to the east, 2 sandhill cranes were reported seen August 18, 3 August 26, and 2 September 4, 1949, by S. V. Wharram.

Family RALLIDAE (Rails, Gallinules, and Coots)

KING RAIL—Rallus elegans elegans Audubon

STATUS—Rare migrant; rare summer resident.

EARLIEST SPRING DATE—April 9, 1941.

LATEST FALL DATE—October 6, 1948.

HABITAT AND DISTRIBUTION—Marshy edges of ponds and streams, and marshes along the Lake Erie shore.

NESTING—This species undoubtedly nested commonly in the region when habitats more to its liking than is the case at present were available. Two recent records are: a nest containing 12 eggs, discovered by R. F. Kukowitch May 15, 1940, in a small cattail swamp of about 500 square feet near Memphis Road, Brooklyn Village; and a nest with 5 eggs found at Warrensville by Rudolph J. Kula May 24, 1931.

VIRGINIA RAIL—Rallus limicola limicola Vieillot

STATUS—Common migrant; locally common summer resident.

EARLIEST SPRING DATE—March 11, 1939. AVERAGE—April 14.

LATEST FALL DATE—October 27, 1934.

An unusually late date is that of a specimen in the CMNH collections taken at Kirtland December 26, 1929.

HABITAT AND DISTRIBUTION—Found in migration and breeding on edges of ponds or marshes where cattails furnish cover. One or more pairs nest regularly in the pond at Forest Lane at North Chagrin. Two to five pairs reported by J. W. Aldrich nesting at Aurora Pond 1932-38. Other breeding records from swamps near Solon, Aurora, and along the Cuyahoga River.

NESTING—Nest built in cattails 12 to 18 inches from ground or water. Construction begins May 6-10. The nest is often perfectly concealed by cattail canopy. Eggs 9 to 11. Incubation period of 11 eggs in nest at North Chagrin was determined by Vera Carrothers to be at least 19 days. Young noted June 9, 11, 12. Young can leave the nest and swim the day they hatch.

49

SORA—Porzana carolina (Linnaeus)

STATUS—Not uncommon migrant; uncommon summer resident.

EARLIEST SPRING DATE—March 21, 1938. AVERAGE—April 23.

LATEST FALL DATE—November 7, 1947.

HABITAT AND DISTRIBUTION—In migration, especially from late April to mid-May, may be found in the vegetation around the edge of almost any inland pond.

NESTING—Breeds only in the larger bogs or ponds. A breeding pair was reported from Lorain County in 1907; Aurora Pond, 1933, 1937, 1938; and Cuyahoga Heights, 1937. May 13, nest, 7 eggs. May 22, 5 eggs. June 7, 7 eggs.

YELLOW RAIL—Coturnicops noveboracensis noveboracensis (Gmelin)

STATUS—Rare migrant; possible rare summer resident.

Wheaton (1882:512) mentions this species as having been "taken in the vicinity of Cleveland." This may refer to the record of Chubb (1880) of April 24, 1880. One was reported seen April 18, 1937, by Ralph A. O'Reilly, Jr., who flushed the bird twice from a wet grassy field in Pepper Pike Village. One was reported seen and heard, near the mouth of the Chagrin River, June 25 and again July 5, 1944, by F. N. Shankland and Roger Davis. In the collections of CMNH are 2 specimens, both taken in the region—a female taken at Brooklyn Heights Village October 12, 1936; and a female picked up in downtown Cleveland September 19, 1943.

HABITAT AND DISTRIBUTION—Wet grassy meadows and marshy borders of ponds or streams are the favorite haunts of this bird.

FLORIDA GALLINULE—Gallinula chloropus cachinnans Bangs

STATUS—Common migrant; uncommon summer resident.

EARLIEST SPRING DATE—April 10, 1943. AVERAGE—April 21.

LATEST FALL DATE—November 26, 1941. AVERAGE—October 25.

HABITAT AND DISTRIBUTION—Edges of small ponds and bogs, and larger marshes.

50

NESTING—One to 3 pairs reported nesting at Aurora Pond from 1932 to 1938. One pair nested at Holden Arboretum in 1939. A pair nested at Twin Lakes (north of Kent in Portage County) in 1947. A nest was discovered on a small island in lake in Aurora Bird Sanctuary in the summer of 1946. Eggs in the nest at Aurora May 21, 1933, and May 27, 1937. Adult with 6 young was reported from Aurora Pond July 2, 1948. Adult with very small young was seen on Corning Lake summer of 1949. On August 22, 1949, adults and two immature birds were seen at Aurora.

AMERICAN COOT—Fulica americana americana Gmelin

STATUS—Common migrant; possible rare summer resident.

EARLIEST SPRING DATE—March 3, 1946. AVERAGE—March 20.

LATEST FALL DATE—Largest migrating flocks are reported November 2 (100) to 20 (450). Records varying from single birds to as many as 60 through December, January, February.

HABITAT AND DISTRIBUTION—In migration may be found on almost any inland pond as well as along the Lake Erie shore.

NESTING—There is no definite nesting record for the region. One bird was present during the summer of 1947 at Aurora Pond. Another bird was reported as staying at Sherwin Pond from July 1939 to January 1941. Adults with young were seen on Corning Lake, summer of 1949. Undoubtedly the coot was a regular breeding bird of the region formerly when suitable marshlands were more available.

Order CHARADRIIFORMES

Family CHARADRIIDAE (Plovers, Turnstones, and Surf-birds)

BELTED PIPING PLOVER—Charadrius melodus circumcinctus (Ridgway)

STATUS—Rare migrant; possible rare summer resident.

EARLIEST SPRING DATE—April 18, 1948. AVERAGE—May 14.

LATEST FALL DATE—September 26 (no year given—Bent 1929:246).

There are but 4 fall dates: August 18, August 22, September 4, and September 24. Kirtland (1874a:170) reported this species as "repeatedly seen" prior to 1852.

HABITAT AND DISTRIBUTION—Almost always seen on open sandy beaches on the Lake Erie shore. Almost all records for the region come from the beaches about the mouth of the Grand River at Fairport Harbor.

NESTING—No nest is made, but the eggs are deposited on the open sand beach where their protective coloration makes them all but invisible. Our only records of the nesting of this bird in the region come from Painesville (probably Richmond Beach), where they have been reported by Doolittle (1934;1923a;1917b:161), as follows: June 18, 1933, nest with 4 eggs. June 21, 1933, nest with 4 eggs. July 4, 1923, 1 pair with 2 young. July 6, 1917, 2 adults and three young. Recent use of this beach for summer colony bathers has probably made it unacceptable for nesting by this plover.

SEMIPALMATED PLOVER—Charadrius hiaticula semipalmatus Bonaparte

STATUS—Common migrant.

EARLIEST SPRING DATE—April 10, 1926. AVERAGE—May 10. LATEST —May 29, 1945.

EARLIEST FALL DATE—July 7, 1931. AVERAGE—August 2. LATEST —November 13, 1938.

This bird is most often recorded on fall migration during August, September, and October. It is most common in the spring during May.

HABITAT AND DISTRIBUTION—Prefers sandy beaches or mud flats on the Lake Erie shore or about inland lakes. In this region it has often been seen at Fairport at the mouth of the Grand River, at White City, and at Shaker Lakes.

NORTHERN KILLDEER—Charadrius vociferus vociferus Linnaeus

STATUS—Common migrant; common summer resident.

EARLIEST SPRING DATE—February 13, 1938. AVERAGE—March 8.

PEAK OF NUMBERS—First two weeks in March.

LATEST FALL DATE—November 28, 1941.

There are several unusual records for late December, and one for January 8, 1946.

HABITAT AND DISTRIBUTION—Typically prefers plowed or open fields, such as playing fields and golf courses; also mud flats about large and small inland lakes. In this region it is regularly to be seen at most of the small lakes, and on almost any large field with little ground cover in the suburban or rural districts.

NESTING—On the ground, in open fields or other exposed places. No nest is usually made, but the eggs are deposited in an open space where their protective coloration makes them all but invisible. Examination of a large number of records shows the earliest egg date to be March 31, and the latest June 28. The greatest number of nesting records are in May, with records of newly hatched young from April 29, May 2, 16, 17, 30; and again from June 25 and 26. These data seem to indicate two broods, one being hatched from the end of April to the first part of May, and the second being hatched toward the end of June or even later.

AMERICAN GOLDEN PLOVER—Pluvialis dominica dominica (Müller)

STATUS—Rare spring migrant; uncommon fall migrant.

ONLY SPRING DATES—April 26, 1880 (Chubb 1880) ; April 27, 1882 (Ingersoll 1882).

The northerly flight of this species in spring passes to the west of our region.

EARLIEST FALL DATE—August 13, 1945. AVERAGE—September 5.

LATEST—November 4, 1948.

HABITAT AND DISTRIBUTION—Frequents sandy beaches on the lake shore, most records coming from Fairport and White City.

BLACK-BELLIED PLOVER—Squatarola squatarola (Linnaeus)

STATUS—Rare spring migrant; uncommon fall migrant.

EARLIEST SPRING DATE—May 16, 1944. AVERAGE—May 25. LATEST —May 28, 1944. Only 4 spring records, all in May.

EARLIEST FALL DATE—August 10, 1942 and 1946. AVERAGE—August 16. LATEST—November 29 (no year given—Bent 1929:170).

HABITAT AND DISTRIBUTION — In this region prefers sandy beaches or mud flats. Seen here most frequently at various points along the Lake Erie shore such as Fairport and White City.

RUDDY TURNSTONE—Arenaria interpres morinella
(Linnaeus)

STATUS—Uncommon migrant.

EARLIEST SPRING DATE—May 2, 1948. AVERAGE—May 19. LATEST —May 30, 1945.

EARLIEST FALL DATE — July 28, 1945. AVERAGE — August 8. LATEST—November 10, 1945.

HABITAT AND DISTRIBUTION—Frequents sandy beaches on the lake shore in this region, most records coming from Fairport and White City.

Family SCOLOPACIDAE (Woodcock, Snipe, and Sandpipers)

AMERICAN WOODCOCK—Philohela minor (Gmelin)

STATUS—Common migrant; common summer resident.

EARLIEST SPRING DATE—February 21, 1880 (Chubb 1880). AVERAGE—March 22.

LATEST FALL DATE—November 25, 1947. AVERAGE—November 13.

HABITAT AND DISTRIBUTION—The marshy edges of ponds, thickets, open moist woods or woods edges, are the favorite haunts of this bird. It is well distributed in favorable locations throughout the region. During the spring migration it often turns up in the most unexpected places.

NESTING—On ground in natural depression. Usually in rather open location or in thin woodlands, often at base of clump of grasses or small tree, or sometimes quite unprotected. A study of 18 records indicates that nesting activities begin as early as March 27, on which date 2 nests have been reported, one containing 4 eggs, the other 2. Nesting continues through April and May and into June, the latest record being for June 17, a nest with 3 eggs. Usual number of eggs is 4.

EUROPEAN WOODCOCK—Scolopax rusticola Linnaeus

STATUS—Rare and accidental visitor.

The only record of this species in our region is that of a bird shot November 6, 1935, by G. F. Dixon, in Newbury Township, Geauga County. The relatively large size of the bird induced Mr.

Dixon to report the matter to Dr. John W. Aldrich of the CMNH. Although parts of the bird had been destroyed, enough remained to make possible positive identification by Dr. Aldrich and Dr. Harry C. Oberholser. Portions of skeleton are in the collections of the Museum (Aldrich 1936b).

WILSON'S SNIPE—Capella gallinago delicata (Ord)

STATUS—Uncommon migrant.

EARLIEST SPRING DATE—March 4, 1880 (Chubb 1880). AVERAGE—March 12. PEAK OF NUMBERS—About April 18. Many May records. LATEST—June 30, 1931.

LATEST FALL DATE—November 22, 1942. PEAK OF NUMBERS—About the middle of October. There is an unusual record of one collected here December 23, 1883 (Ingersoll 1884).

Due to the fact that there are a number of June, July and August records, it is difficult to determine latest spring and earliest fall occurrence. Though it has never been reported as nesting in the region, this is not an impossibility.

HABITAT AND DISTRIBUTION—Marshy edges of ponds or streams in rather open situations are the preferred habitat of this bird. It is well distributed over the region during the migration period wherever there are suitable locations.

LONG-BILLED CURLEW—Numenius americanus americanus Bechstein

STATUS—Rare and accidental visitor.

We have 3 records of the occurrence of this northwesterly breeding species in our region. In connection with Dr. Kirtland's report on the collection of some marbled godwits at Fairport prior to August 1, 1840, he says, "They were associating with a flock of long-billed curlews (*Numenius longirostris*)" (Wheaton 1882:220). Chubb (1880) lists this species as arriving April 24, 1880, this record being based on his personal observation. Bent (1929:108) lists September 15 as the date of "late . . . departure" of this species from the region of Cleveland.

HUDSONIAN CURLEW—Numenius phaeopus hudsonicus Latham

STATUS—Rare and accidental visitor.

Wheaton (1882:220) quotes Kirtland as follows: "I have a specimen in my cabinet that alighted in the garden of Mr. A. Hayden, of this city, and was shot by him three years since (1837?)." More recent records of the occurrence of this species in the region, ranging from July 10 through August and September to October 6, are the following: Hadeler (1924) reported it July 14, 1922; July 15, 1923; and July 10, August 1, 2, 1924, at Painesville. Two were reported July 16, 1940, at Fairport by R. W. Hill. One August 28, 1945, at White City, by Vera Carrothers. One September 21, 1941, at Richmond by A. T. Burch. From September 18 to October 6, 1945, at least 2 birds were regularly recorded at White City by Carrothers, Hill, Morse and Ramisch. July 18, 1948, one seen near Coast Guard Station at Richmond Beach by George King.

HABITAT AND DISTRIBUTION—Lake Erie shore, Fairport to White City.

ESKIMO CURLEW—Numenius borealis (Forster)

STATUS—Probably extinct at the present time.

Mention of this now vanished species occurs in the "Family Visitor" (1851,2:68) in these words: "During the last week a beautiful specimen of the rare Esquimaux Curlew was sent to us by Esq. Bramun of Avon." As Dr. Kirtland was chief editor of the "Family Visitor", published at Cleveland and Hudson, we may infer that he is authority for the record. Wheaton (1882 :493) quotes R. K. Winslow, of Cleveland, as saying that the Eskimo Curlew was not rare here.

UPLAND PLOVER—Bartramia longicauda (Bechstein)

STATUS—Uncommon migrant; uncommon summer resident.

EARLIEST SPRING DATE—March 28, 1929. AVERAGE—April 15.

LATEST FALL DATE—September 30, 1947.

HABITAT AND DISTRIBUTION—Prefers open fields, devoid of trees. Generally distributed over the region in localities which meet its nesting requirements. For instance, 4 pairs were found nesting in a 40-acre area of high prairie type grassland in 1939.

NESTING—On the ground, usually in the midst of a clump of weedy plants. May 6, nest, 4 eggs. May 12, nest with eggs. May 28, nest, 4 eggs, bird incubating; June 7, three young in nest, one still wet from hatching, one hiding about a foot distant from nest. June 4, nest with 4 newly hatched young. June 8, 4 eggs.

SPOTTED SANDPIPER—Actitis macularia (Linnaeus)

STATUS—Common migrant; common summer resident.

EARLIEST SPRING DATE—March 29, 1912. AVERAGE—April 20.

LATEST FALL DATE—October 18, 1942. AVERAGE—September 21.

HABITAT AND DISTRIBUTION — Prefers margins of ponds, lakes and streams. Well distributed in suitable locations throughout the region.

NESTING—Nest on ground, usually in close proximity to water, frequently at base of clump of vegetation. Nests have been found on sand dunes of Lake Erie shore, in fallow field, on face of cliff overlooking lake, in scrubby field near small pond, on shale bar at edge of Rocky River, in marshy spot in old ox-bow of Cuyahoga River. May 19, nest and eggs. May 20, nest, 4 eggs. June 3, nest, 4 eggs; June 20, 3 young hatched. June 6, 4 eggs. June 7, nest, 4 eggs.

EASTERN SOLITARY SANDPIPER—Tringa solitaria solitaria Wilson

STATUS—Common migrant.

EARLIEST SPRING DATE—April 8, 1945. AVERAGE—May 6. LATEST —June 7, 1941.

EARLIEST FALL DATE—June 23, 1947. LATEST—November 19, 1927. AVERAGE—September 19.

HABITAT AND DISTRIBUTION—Prefers margins of lakes, ponds, streams, open fields and marshes. Well distributed throughout the region.

NESTING — The fact that we have a number of June and July records of occurrence would indicate that nesting territories may be not far removed from this region.

WESTERN WILLET—Catoptrophorus semipalmatus inornatus (Brewster)

STATUS—Uncommon migrant.

Reports of the willet (*C. s. semipalmatus*) by Dr. Kirtland as a common visitor to the shore of Lake Erie must refer to the western form, now known as *C. s. inornatus*. Of this species Dr. Kirtland, as reported by Wheaton (1882:220), says: "This bird is a common visitor to the shores of Lake Erie, both in the spring and autumn. On the 3d of July, 1838, I shot an old specimen from a flock of more than twenty individuals, that were in the habit of visiting the marsh in Ohio City (now Cleveland), at the mouth of the Cuyahoga, for a number of days in succession. The young birds appeared here on the first of July of the present year, and considerable numbers have been shot by the sportsmen. A few years since, they remained here during the whole of the summer, and probably reared their young in the neighborhood."

Later records of occurrence are: May 8, 1948(1) (King and Morse); July 18, 1945(4) (Foley and Stevens); August 11, 1944 (11) (Carrothers); August 12, 1917(1) (Doolittle 1917b:162); August 19, 1945(1) (Godfrey); September 3-10, 1944(1) (Carrothers); September 8, 1936(1) (Akers and Spare) (Baird 1936:470).

HABITAT AND DISTRIBUTION—Has been observed along the Lake Erie shore at White City, Fairport Harbor, and as indicated above, at the mouth of the Cuyahoga River July 3, 1838.

GREATER YELLOWLEGS—Totanus melanoleucus (Gmelin)

STATUS—Common migrant.

EARLIEST SPRING DATE — March 21, 1938. AVERAGE — May 9. LATEST—June 12, 1948.

EARLIEST FALL DATE — August 8, 1948. LATEST—November 17, 1941. AVERAGE—September 22.

HABITAT AND DISTRIBUTION—Found along the margins of lakes, ponds and streams throughout the region. Prefers mud flats.

LESSER YELLOWLEGS—Totanus flavipes (Gmelin)

STATUS—Common migrant.

EARLIEST SPRING DATE—March 21, 1938. AVERAGE — April 12. LATEST—June 12, 1948.

EARLIEST FALL DATE—July 13, 1940. AVERAGE—August 7. LATEST —November 17, 1941.

HABITAT AND DISTRIBUTION—Prefers margins of ponds and lakes, especially where mud flats are found. Well distributed over the region during migration wherever its preferred habitat is available.

AMERICAN KNOT—Calidris canutus rufa (Wilson)

STATUS—Rare migrant.

The only records of the occurrence of this species within our regional boundaries are the following: May 15, 1927 ("a flock") at Fairport (Simmons 1927:56); August 13, 1945(1), White City (Foley and Stevens); August 26(2), 28(1), 29(1), and September 3(1), 1944, at White City (Adams and Spare); September 12, 1933, North Chagrin (A. B. Williams); September 20(1), 21(1), 22(1), 1940, Fairport (Fuller, Morse, Dobbins).

HABITAT AND DISTRIBUTION—All but one of the above records are for the Lake Erie shore. The North Chagrin record is for a small inland pond.

PURPLE SANDPIPER—Erolia maritima (Brünnich)

STATUS—Rare spring, fall and winter visitor.

Wheaton (1882:476) mentions this species as a very rare visitor on Lake Erie. He says that Winslow told him that a specimen was taken many years prior to 1882 at Cleveland. H. E. Chubb is said to have taken a Cleveland specimen September 11, 1883, No. 47105 in the Museum of Zoology, University of Michigan (Swales 1918:1). All of the more recent records are from Fairport Harbor or Richmond Beach. The earliest of these were reported by Doolittle (1916; 1917a; 1924a)—all single birds— seen October 29 and November 12, 1916; October 25, 1922; November 11, 1923. Other records have been summarized by Hill (1943). These are: 1937, December 27(1); 1938, January 2(1),

November 13(4), 19(2), 20(3); 1941, December 27(1), 31(3); 1942, November 27(1). Motion pictures in color of one of these birds were taken by Hill and serve as an additional check on identification. Still other records are: December 22, 1941. December 22, 1948, January 2, 3, 4, 8, 9, 16, 1949, single birds, or occasionally 2, seen by numerous observers at White City. March 21, 22, 1949, one seen at White City by Carrothers.

PECTORAL SANDPIPER—*Erolia melanotos* (Vieillot)

STATUS—Common migrant.

EARLIEST SPRING DATE — March 18, 1945. AVERAGE—April 25. PEAK OF NUMBERS—May. LATEST—May 24, 1941.

EARLIEST FALL DATE—July 22, 1946. AVERAGE—August 8. LATEST —November 2, 1946.

HABITAT AND DISTRIBUTION—Prefers margins of lakes, ponds, and streams, especially where mud flats are found. Well distributed over the region during migration wherever suitable habitats occur.

WHITE-RUMPED SANDPIPER—*Erolia fuscicollis* (Vieillot)

STATUS—Rare migrant.

Records of the occurrence of this sandpiper within or near our regional boundaries are the following: May 4, 1931, 2 seen at Shaker Lake (Gilliland); May 12(1), 19(2), 1946, at Richmond Beach; August 19, 1948, 1 seen at Mosquito Creek (Hamann); September 30, 1945, 1 seen at White City (King, Hall); October 6, 1945, 1 seen at Richmond Beach (Hill); October 13, 1946, 2 seen at Lake Dorothy (Lieftinck); October 20, 1940; October 23, 1948, 6 seen at Mosquito Creek (Hill).

BAIRD'S SANDPIPER—*Erolia bairdii* (Coues)

STATUS—Uncommon migrant.

ONLY SPRING DATES—April 25, 1913; May 8 (no year given—Bent 1927:200).

EARLIEST FALL DATE—July 27, 1913. AVERAGE—August 21. PEAK OF NUMBERS—September. LATEST—November 25, 1933.

HABITAT AND DISTRIBUTION—Prefers uplands near shores of lakes or ponds, especially where mud flats are found. Most records come from the Lake Erie shore.

LEAST SANDPIPER—Erolia minutilla (Vieillot)

STATUS—Not uncommon migrant.

EARLIEST SPRING DATE—April 17, 1945. AVERAGE—May 6. PEAK OF NUMBERS—May. LATEST—May 30, 1945.

EARLIEST FALL DATE—June 12, 1948. AVERAGE—August 2. PEAK OF NUMBERS—August. LATEST—October 7, 1945.

HABITAT AND DISTRIBUTION—Prefers margins of lakes and ponds or streams, particularly where mud flats are found. Well distributed where suitable habitats are available.

RED-BACKED SANDPIPER—Erolia alpina pacifica (Coues)

STATUS—Not uncommon migrant.

EARLIEST SPRING DATE—April 16, 1938. AVERAGE—May 14. LATEST —May 30, 1945.

EARLIEST FALL DATE—July 25, 1898. AVERAGE—September 19. PEAK OF NUMBERS—October. LATEST—November 20, 1941.

Probably formerly much more abundant than now. Wheaton (1882:478) calls it a common spring and fall migrant. Kirtland mentions "large flocks" seen "last autumn" (1839?) (Wheaton 1882:219).

HABITAT AND DISTRIBUTION—Prefers margins of ponds and lakes, especially where mud flats are found. Well distributed over the region wherever its preferred habitat is available.

EASTERN DOWITCHER—Limnodromus griseus griseus (Gmelin)

STATUS—Rare migrant.

ONLY SPRING DATES—April 24, 1935 and April 26, 1936 (2 birds each); May 17, 1942.

EARLIEST FALL DATE—July 18, 1942 and 1945. AVERAGE (of 5 July dates)—July 23 (1 or 2 birds each date). LATEST—October 13, 1940.

61

HABITAT AND DISTRIBUTION—Shores of ponds and lakes. Records include Lake Erie shore at White City and small pond at North Chagrin.

STILT SANDPIPER—Micropalama himantopus (Bonaparte)

STATUS—Rare migrant.

The records of the occurrence of this sandpiper within our regional limits are as follows: July 29, 1917, one seen near Painesville by Doolittle (1917b:162); May 3, 1942, one seen at Richmond, reported by A. B. Fuller; August 17, 1947, one seen at Upper Shaker Lake by Donald Newman; August 23, 1939, 2 seen at Holden Arboretum by B. P. Bole, Jr.; September 23, 1945, 2 seen at Lake Dorothy by J. E. Lieftinck. It is not infrequently reported from nearby localities just east of our region.

HABITAT AND DISTRIBUTION—Shores of ponds and lakes, particularly where mud flats are found.

SEMIPALMATED SANDPIPER—Ereunetes pusillus (Linnaeus)

STATUS—Common migrant.

EARLIEST SPRING DATE—May 4, 1947. LATEST—June 5, 1942 and 1946.

EARLIEST FALL DATE—July 13, 1940. AVERAGE—July 21. PEAK OF NUMBERS—August. LATEST—October 9, 1948.

HABITAT AND DISTRIBUTION—Prefers margins of lakes, ponds and streams, especially where mud flats are found. Widely distributed throughout the region in suitable habitats.

WESTERN SANDPIPER—Ereunetes mauri Cabanis

STATUS—Rare migrant.

We have no spring records for this species within our regional limits.

EARLIEST FALL DATE—July 16, 1946. LATEST—September 9, 1941.

HABITAT AND DISTRIBUTION—Records are from Fairport, White City and the Akron Lakes. Usually seen in company with other shorebirds on mud flats and on the Lake Erie shore.

BUFF-BREASTED SANDPIPER—Tryngites subruficollis (Vieillot)

STATUS—Rare migrant.
No spring records.

EARLIEST FALL DATE—August 19, 1923. LATEST—September 18, 1948.

Our only records of this sandpiper, rare in our region, are the following: August 19, 20, 1923, one reported seen on the Lake Erie beach north of Painesville (Doolittle 1923b); August 31, September 1, 2, 1945, one seen on each of these dates at White City by Vera Carrothers and W. Earl Godfrey; autumn of 1839, 2 specimens collected by Kirtland at Cleveland (Wheaton 1882: 219). In addition to these records within the region is the report of 5 seen September 12, and 2 September 18, 1948, at Mosquito Creek, just east of our limits.

HABITAT AND DISTRIBUTION—Margins of lakes and ponds, particularly Lake Erie shore.

MARBLED GODWIT—Limosa fedoa (Linnaeus)

STATUS—Rare and accidental migrant.

The only record of this species in our region is that of 2 collected at Fairport prior to August 1, 1840, and presented to Dr. Kirtland, who says: "The Hon. Mr. Granger has furnished me with a beautiful pair, killed near his residence at Fairport. Several young specimens were shot in this vicinity about the first of August of the present season." Dated Cleveland, Ohio, June 4, 1840. (Wheaton 1882:220).

HUDSONIAN GODWIT—Limosa haemastica (Linnaeus)

STATUS—Rare and accidental migrant.

Our only knowledge of the occurrence of this rare wading bird in our region is Wheaton's assertion that its occurrence near Cleveland was noted by Winslow. This would place the record prior to 1880 (Wheaton 1882:481).

A recent record just outside our region to the west is that of one seen May 19, 1946, near Sandusky, by J. E. Lieftinck.

SANDERLING—Crocethia alba (Pallas)

STATUS—Common fall migrant; rare in spring.

EARLIEST SPRING DATE—May 12, 1940. AVERAGE—May 18. LATEST —May 28, 1948.

EARLIEST FALL DATE—July 7, 1942. AVERAGE—July 20. PEAK OF NUMBERS—Late August and September (flocks of 40-125). LATEST—November 18, 1945.

HABITAT AND DISTRIBUTION—Usually seen along the Lake Erie shore, although sometimes on margins of inland ponds.

Family RECURVIROSTRIDAE (Avocets and Stilts)

BLACK-NECKED STILT—Himantopus mexicanus (Müller)

STATUS—Rare and accidental visitor.

Records of this species in our region are limited to the following: Wheaton (1882:463) says: "The Stilt has been repeatedly taken on Lake Erie, as I am informed by Mr. Winslow." Mr. A. Hall of Lakewood reported a black-necked stilt shot by him October 24, 1881, at Berea (Jones 1904b:112. A dead bird, reported to be of this species, was noted by Omar E. Mueller, August 15, 1941, on the pavement of North Park Boulevard near the Lower Shaker Lake, Cleveland Heights. Unfortunately this specimen was not preserved.

Family PHALAROPODIDAE (Phalaropes)

RED PHALAROPE—Phalaropus fulicarius (Linnaeus)

STATUS—Rare and accidental visitor.

Wheaton (1882:467) says that R. K. Winslow informed him in 1861 that 2 or 3 specimens had been taken on Lake Erie. Later records are: October 21, 1930, one seen on the Grand River about 3 miles from Lake Erie (Doolittle 1931:225); November 25, 1945, one seen at White City by R. W. Hill and M. E. Morse; November 26-30, 1948, one repeatedly seen by many observers on a small lagoon on the Lake Erie shore near Edgewater Park; November 28, 29, 1948, one seen at White City by Vera Carrothers and M. Owen Davies; November 8, 1949, one collected at Fairport by James F. Akers.

WILSON'S PHALAROPE—Steganopus tricolor Vieillot

STATUS—Rare and accidental visitor.

The only record of this western species in our region is contained in a reference by Wheaton (1882:464). He says it was reported by Winslow as having been repeatedly taken in the vicinity of Cleveland. The probability is that prior to 1882 (the date of Wheaton's report) this bird, then a common nesting species in northern Indiana and northern Illinois, might not have been an uncommon visitor to the Cleveland region. It is still recorded as a "fairly regular, though not numerous, transient" near Toledo (Campbell 1940:83).

NORTHERN PHALAROPE—Lobipes lobatus (Linnaeus)

STATUS—Rare and accidental visitor.

The only records of this sub-Arctic bird in our region are as follows: Kirtland says that a bird of this species "was shot on Lake Erie, near the pier of Cleveland harbor, last November (1839?), by a young man in my employment . . . The phalarope was a young bird in winter plumage. It is preserved in my cabinet." (Wheaton 1882:217). Wheaton (1882:467) says: "Mr. Winslow and others have . . . taken it on the lake shore." E. A. Doolittle (1918:118) reported seeing one, probably at Fairport, September 29, 1918.

October 13, 1944, Edith Dobbins reported seeing 2 swimming inside the breakwater at Edgewater Park on Lake Erie. September 8, 1945, eleven were reported seen on Mosquito Creek Reservoir just outside our region to the east. Identified by Carrothers and Smith. (Mayfield 1946:7). Two were reported at the same place (Mosquito Creek) September 16, and 1 September 23, 1945, by W. Earl Godfrey. One was reported August 19, 1948, also at Mosquito Creek, by Carl F. Hamann.

Family STERCORARIIDAE (Jaegers and Skuas)

POMARINE JAEGER—Stercorarius pomarinus (Temminck)

STATUS—Rare winter visitor.

The only records we have of this Arctic and north Atlantic sea bird in our region are the following: Wheaton (1882:546) mentions a male of this species collected by H. E. Chubb at Cleveland in the fall of 1880. One was reported seen at Lakewood December 19, 1925 (Moulton and Derbaum 1926). One was collected for the CMNH at Fairport on October 15, 1945, by Rudolph J. Kula. One was reported seen at White City October 6, 1945, by Rudolph J. Kula and Raymond W. Hill.

PARASITIC JAEGER—Stercorarius parasiticus (Linnaeus)

STATUS—Rare winter visitor.

The first record of this Arctic and Atlantic sea bird in our region is that of one taken at the mouth of Rocky River in November, 1857; another was reported shot by Hingartner near Lorain (after 1880) (Jones 1903:27). More recently one was reported by Doolittle (1919e:127) as found dead on the beach at Fairport September 20, 1914. Another dead bird was picked up by Doolittle (1924a) near the same spot at Fairport October 7, 1923. Doolittle (1931:225) further reported observing a bird in the black phase of plumage flying low over the water at Fairport August 17, 1930.

The fall and winter of 1945 saw a veritable incursion of these birds along the Lake Erie shore. From October 2 to December 8, one to three birds of this species were seen almost daily from Gordon Park to Richmond Beach, including White City. They were observed by practically all of the amateur and professional ornithologists of Cleveland. On October 6 a dead immature female was picked up and sent to the CMNH. On October 15 one was collected for the Museum by Rudolph J. Kula. Although no more than 3 birds were seen at any one time, their distribution and frequency of appearance suggest many more than these.

In 1946 single individuals were seen at Richmond Beach September 18 by A. B. Fuller; at White City September 21 by Margarette E. Morse; and at Fairport September 22 by W. Earl Godfrey. One killed in Bratenahl September 21, now in CMNH collection.

Family LARIDAE (Gulls and Terns)

GLAUCOUS GULL—Larus hyperboreus hyperboreus Gunnerus

STATUS—Uncommon winter visitor.

Thirteen reports of the occurrence of this gull in our region range from December 25 (1947) to March 23 (1948). All records but one are of single individuals. One record is of 2. From December 25, 1947, to February 29, 1948, one or two birds were seen regularly along the lake shore at Cleveland.

HABITAT AND DISTRIBUTION—All observations of this gull have been made along the Lake Erie shore from Gordon Park to Edgewater Park.

NORTHERN ICELAND GULL—Larus leucopterus leucopterus Vieillot

STATUS—Rare and occasional winter visitor.

Records are for December, January and February.

Mentioned as occurring occasionally in winter near Cleveland prior to 1882 (Wheaton 1882:547). A specimen, collected December 22, 1888, at Lorain, is in the Oberlin College Museum (Jones 1903:28). More recent records are the following: December 3, 1916, an immature bird reported seen at Fairport Harbor (Doolittle 1917a). December 25, 1947, to January 18, 1948, one repeatedly seen by numerous observers on the lakefront near Gordon Park. January 30, 1937, one adult bird reported seen (Baird 1937:170). February 20, 1942, one reported seen by W. E. Godfrey. February 24, 1946, one reported seen by R. W. Hill. The last 3 records above all refer to the lakefront near Gordon Park.

HABITAT AND DISTRIBUTION—Reported only from the Lake Erie shore.

GREAT BLACK-BACKED GULL—Larus marinus Linnaeus

STATUS—Not uncommon winter visitor.

Closer attention to the gulls along the Lake Erie shore in winter in recent years has disclosed the fact that from 1 to 14 individuals of this Atlantic coastal gull may be more or less regularly found at such places as Lorain Harbor, Clifton Park, Gordon Park and Fairport Harbor. Dates range from December 23 (1945) to March 19 (1944). An unusual record is that of 2 seen at Avon-on-the-Lake August 25, 1947. From December 29, 1944, to February 11, 1945, the species was regularly reported along the lakefront in groups ranging from 2 to 21. Largest numbers appeared during the coldest weather. In 1948 it was recorded regularly from January 11 to February 29 (1-4). The species was reported as an "occasional visitor" in the vicinity of Cleveland by Winslow as far back as 1880 (Wheaton 1882:547).

HABITAT AND DISTRIBUTION—Reported only from the Lake Erie shore.

AMERICAN HERRING GULL—Larus argentatus smithsonianus Coues

STATUS—Locally abundant migrant; abundant winter visitor.

While we have records of this species for every month in the year, the lake shore is practically deserted by herring gulls during June and July. They do not usually become numerous until September. From this time on they become common, the flocks often including hundreds. Greatest numbers occur in December, January and February.

During the winter of 1941-42 a careful week by week census of the waterfowl along the Lake Erie shore from Rocky River to East 140th Street, made by members of the Kirtland Bird Club, recorded an influx of 3367 herring gulls to this area January 31 and February 1, 1942. Previous to that time the high number had been 631 for December 20, 21, 1941. The week following resulted in a count of 866.

An unusual record is that for January 10 and 11, 1948, when gulls were so numerous along the lake shore it was impossible to count them. R. W. Hill estimated them at 30,000 from Edgewater Park to White City. These flocks included herring, ring-billed and Bonaparte's gulls.

HABITAT AND DISTRIBUTION—While seen in greatest numbers along the Lake Erie shore, herring gulls are frequently seen on the inland lakes of the region as well as occasionally in the Rocky River and Cuyahoga Valleys.

NESTING—The nesting record nearest to our region is of one on Chicken Island (near Put-in-Bay, Lake Erie) June 16, 1926, 3 eggs (Arthur B. Fuller).

RING-BILLED GULL—Larus delawarensis Ord

STATUS—Locally abundant migrant; abundant winter visitor.

While there are records for every month in the year, this species seems to be most numerous in May and August. Beginning in late July its numbers gradually increase through August (1000 recorded August 26, 1940). While numbers are subject to considerable fluctuation, they are usually well maintained through the winter.

HABITAT AND DISTRIBUTION—Appears in greatest numbers along the Lake Erie shore, where it is associated closely with the herring gulls. It also is occasionally seen on the small inland lakes and rivers.

FRANKLIN'S GULL—Larus pipixcan Wagler

STATUS—Rare and accidental fall and winter visitor.

The records of occurrence of this western gull in our region are as follows: September 14, November 3, 1940, one reported seen at Gordon Park by Al Bohn; October 20, 1940, one reported seen at White City by Donald L. Newman; October 25, 1940, one reported seen at White City by M. B. Skaggs; November 11 (1), and November 12 (2), 1939, seen at Cleveland lakefront by M. B. Skaggs; November 20, 1948, two seen at Cleveland lakefront by J. E. Lieftinck and W. L. Towle; December 10, 1939, one reported seen on Cleveland lakefront by Ralph A. O'Reilly, Jr.; December 22, 1930, one reported seen at Fairport by E. A.Doolittle (1931:227); January 8, 1931, one reported seen at Fairport by John W. Aldrich (probably the same bird reported by Doolittle December 22, 1930); November 7, 1931, one inside the breakwater east of Edgewater Park reported by S. C. Kendeigh.

HABITAT AND DISTRIBUTION—Reported only from the Lake Erie shore.

BONAPARTE'S GULL—Larus philadelphia (Ord)

STATUS—Locally common migrant; common winter visitor.

Migrating flocks along the Lake Erie shore build up in numbers through March, April and May. There are very few records for June and July, but immature birds are likely to appear by mid-July. Largest numbers are seen from late August through December, when flocks estimated at 2000, 3000, 4500 and 8000 have been reported. On January 10 and 11, 1948, an estimated 30,000 gulls, including many Bonaparte's, were present along the Cleveland lakefront from White City to Edgewater Park (R. W. Hill). By the middle of January this heavy migration period is past. A few birds usually spend the winter.

HABITAT AND DISTRIBUTION—Greatest concentrations of numbers are along the Lake Erie shore in such places as the harbor at Lorain, the mouth of Rocky River, Gordon Park and Fairport Harbor. Bonaparte's gulls are also not infrequently seen on small inland lakes during migration periods.

LITTLE GULL—Larus minutus Pallas

STATUS—Rare and accidental visitor.

There is a record of this European species in our region, based on about an hour's observation, reported as having been seen (probably at Fairport) December 29, 1923 (Doolittle 1924b). Another sight record of the little gull was made at Avon-on-the-Lake, January 31, and February 1, 1949, by James F. Akers and Frank M. Phelps of Elyria, both of whom had abundant opportunity to study the bird under the most favorable conditions.

ATLANTIC KITTIWAKE—Rissa tridactyla tridactyla (Linnaeus)

STATUS—Rare and accidental winter visitor.

Wheaton (1882:550) says: "Mr. Winslow notes the occurrence of three specimens in Cleveland harbor many years since" (prior to 1880). More recently, November 23, 1944, a bird of this species was reported seen at White City by Gordon Spare; and again on December 21, 1947, another was reported seen at the lakefront at 71st Street first by Jerry Piskac and later by R. W. Hill, Vera Carrothers, Margaret E. Perner and Ray Smiley.

70

SABINE'S GULL—Xema sabini sabini (Sabine)

STATUS—Rare and accidental visitor.

We have one record of this Arctic species in the region. Wheaton (1882:552) says: "Mr. Winslow informs me that he took an immature bird of this species in Cleveland harbor many years since (earlier than 1880). The specimen was preserved and mounted, and placed in the museum of the Cleveland Medical College."

GULL-BILLED TERN—Gelochelidon nilotica aranea (Wilson)

STATUS—Rare and accidental visitor.

Wheaton (1882:553) mentions this species as a "Rare visitor in the vicinity of Cleveland, where taken by Mr. Winslow." This would be prior to 1880. B. P. Bole, Jr., who is familiar with this tern as he has seen it in Cuba and Jamaica, says he and Dr. Z. B. Adams of Brookline, Massachusetts, saw one at Fairport Harbor in July 1938.

FORSTER'S TERN—Sterna forsteri Nuttall

STATUS—Rare and accidental migrant.

The records of the occurrence of this tern here are as follows: April 27, 1941, one reported at Gordon Park by B. P. Bole, Jr.; May 9, 1937, one reported seen at Mentor Headlands by Arthur B. Fuller and C. M. Shipman; September 22, 1937, one reported seen at Painesville by Hicks (Walker 1937:473). August 29, 1948, two seen at Fairport, reported by George King; August 29, 30, 1944, one reported seen at White City on both dates by Gordon Spare; September 27, 28, 1947, one reported seen at White City by Vera Carrothers, R. W. Hill, Margarette E. Morse and Donald L. Newman; October 4, 5, 1947, four reported seen October 4 and one October 5 at White City by Vera Carrothers, R. W. Hill, Margarette E. Morse and Donald L. Newman. Another record just outside our regional limits to the west is the report of 2 seen at Bay Point (Sandusky region) September 24, 1941, by W. Earl Godfrey.

COMMON TERN—Sterna hirundo hirundo Linnaeus

STATUS—Common migrant.

EARLIEST SPRING DATE—April 5, 1948. AVERAGE—April 16. PEAK OF NUMBERS—May 16. LATEST—June 12, 1946.

There are a few scattering June records. Birds reappear in late July, and numbers increase through August and September.

LATEST FALL DATE—November 27, 1948.

HABITAT AND DISTRIBUTION—Greatest concentrations of numbers are along the Lake Erie shore. Also seen occasionally on inland lakes.

NESTING—The nesting colony nearest to our region is on Starve Island in Lake Erie near Put-in-Bay. Nests on bare rock or sand beach. May 28, 1928, many nests with 1 to 5 eggs.

ROSEATE TERN—Sterna dougallii dougallii Montagu

STATUS—Rare and accidental visitor.

There is one record for this Atlantic coastal bird in our region, reported by Doolittle (1920a:65) for the Lake Erie shore (probably at Fairport) July 31, 1919.

CASPIAN TERN—Hydroprogne caspia (Pallas)

STATUS—Uncommon migrant.

EARLIEST SPRING DATE — April 18, 1947. AVERAGE — April 21. LATEST—May 23, 1948.

EARLIEST FALL DATE—July 13, 1940. LATEST—September 26, 1937.

HABITAT AND DISTRIBUTION—Seen most frequently along the Lake Erie shore, but occasionally on smaller inland lakes.

BLACK TERN—Chlidonias niger surinamensis (Gmelin)

STATUS—Uncommon migrant; possible rare summer resident.

EARLIEST SPRING DATE — April 23, 1947. AVERAGE — May 11. LATEST—May 31, 1924.

Birds reappear about mid-July. On August 15, 1912, large numbers passing overhead, apparently migrating, were reported at Gates Mills by Mrs. F. H. Ginn of that village.

LATEST FALL DATE—October 13, 1946.

HABITAT AND DISTRIBUTION—While usually seen along the Lake Erie shore, black terns have been reported from the smaller inland lakes, particularly Corning Lake and Aurora Pond. It is a summer resident in the Sandusky region.

Family ALCIDAE (Auks, Murres, and Puffins)

BRÜNNICH'S MURRE—Uria lomvia lomvia (Linnaeus)

STATUS—Rare and accidental winter visitor.

There are two records of the occurrence of this North Atlantic sea bird in our region. Following a heavy storm from the northeast December 18, 1896, a number of these birds were swept far inland, appearing in a dazed condition in various bodies of water, or helplessly stranded in the fields of northern Ohio and neighboring localities (Dawson 1903:639). Two of these birds were picked up by J. M. Keck of Mentor (in his yard, according to F. N. Shankland). One of these was purchased for the Oberlin College Museum (Jones 1897), the other went to the Museum of Lake Erie College, Painesville (Doolittle 1924c).

Another record of a single individual of this species was reported by Doolittle (1924c), who identified the bird at close quarters swimming near the end of the breakwater at Fairport December 12, 1920.

Order COLUMBIFORMES

Family COLUMBIDAE (Pigeons and Doves)

ROCK DOVE—Columba livia Gmelin

STATUS—Common permanent resident.

In the last 25 years the domestic pigeon has really become a wild bird in this region, in the sense that it is independent of the care of man and rears its young successfully in an essentially wild state.

HABITAT AND DISTRIBUTION—A common year-round resident of many of the city parks and of certain busy street intersections, such as the Public Square, Superior and East 9th Street, and

Euclid and 105th Street, City of Cleveland. It also nests under the eaves of houses in certain suburban residence sections.

NESTING—A loose pile of trash placed on ledges and sills or in cornices and crannies of buildings. This bird has provided us with what is undoubtedly the earliest breeding record for the region. On February 19, 1941, a young dove, as yet incapable of flight, fell from the cornice of the Cleveland Trust Company building at the corner of Euclid Avenue and East 9th Street, Cleveland, and was brought to the Museum of Natural History. The egg from which it was hatched must have been laid about January 15. Spring and fall nestings are not uncommon. January 27, 1943, a pair of doves was observed carrying nesting materials to a ledge under the cornice of a house on Scarborough Road, Cleveland Heights. This proved to be a successful nesting.

EASTERN MOURNING DOVE—Zenaidura macroura carolinensis (Linnaeus)

STATUS—Common migrant; common summer resident.

EARLIEST SPRING DATE—March 3, 1945. AVERAGE—March 14.

Where there is a suitable food supply, small flocks may remain throughout the winter, as, for example, a group of 24 birds which wintered in a field of standing corn near Willoughby in 1941. Lone birds often frequent winter feeding stations. Two flocks of about 20 each wintered at Brecksville in 1948-49.

HABITAT AND DISTRIBUTION—Frequents thorn scrub fields, open woodlots, orchards, and suburban regions where there are shade trees. Generally distributed over the area, occurring in both the City and Metropolitan Parks.

NESTING—The nest, a flat pile of twigs, which are often so scattered that the eggs show through the bottom, is located usually from 5 to 15 feet above the ground in small trees, particularly evergreens and hawthorns, or on arbors, trellises, and outbuildings. Sometimes this species utilizes old abandoned robins' nests. March 12, bird returns to old robin's nest under eaves of building which she had occupied in two previous years; March 15, begins building; March 26, incubating 2 eggs; April 26, 2 young leave nest. April 16, nest begun in old robin's nest 30 feet up in maple tree. April 20, nest being constructed in small spruce tree; April 26, bird incubating 2 eggs; May 20, 2 young in nest;

May 23, young left nest. April 25, 2 eggs in nest in spruce tree about 5 feet from ground. Sometimes as many as 3 broods may be raised in a season.

PASSENGER PIGEON—Ectopistes migratorius (Linnaeus)

STATUS—Now extinct. Formerly an abundant migrant and locally abundant summer resident.

The last living specimen of this species died in the Cincinnati Zoo September 1, 1914. The CMNH has 8 mounted specimens, one of which was collected "400 yards east of Doan Brook" on the Brooker farm in 1886. Dr. R. C. Rush of Hudson is authority for the statement that the last passenger pigeon seen in Hudson was one shot by Frank Hodge there in 1889. The former abundance of the bird here may be inferred from the following excerpt from the "Family Visitor" of July 8, 1851, edited by Dr. J. P. Kirtland: "Unusual flights of Wild Pigeons have been observed along the south shore of the lake during the present summer. Great numbers have been killed in various ways, and as they have been mostly young and fat, they have become a popular article of food among epicures. Since our cherries commenced ripening, these birds have resorted to our orchards and shown a most voracious propensity to devour the fruits. So eager are they that the discharge of a gun into their ranks will hardly frighten them from the premises . . . the structure of the Telegraph lines in our vicinity is daily endangered by the weight of these birds settling upon the wires." (Kirtland 1851).

Order PSITTACIFORMES

Family PSITTACIDAE (Parrots, Paroquets, and Macaws)

LOUISIANA PAROQUET—Conuropsis carolinensis ludovicianus (Gmelin)

STATUS—Now probably extinct.

Read (1853b:400) says: "A few years ago a flock of these birds appeared in Tallmadge, Summit county, as I was informed by my friend Rev. Samuel Wright." This constitutes the only basis for including the bird in our list. Ridgway (1916:147) gives the range of this species as "Formerly inhabiting the entire

75

Mississippi Valley (except open prairies and plains) from West Virginia to eastern Colorado, north to southern shores of Lake Erie."

Order CUCULIFORMES

Family CUCULIDAE (Cuckoos, Roadrunners, and Anis)

YELLOW-BILLED CUCKOO—Coccyzus americanus americanus (Linnaeus)

STATUS—Common migrant; common summer resident.

EARLIEST SPRING DATE—April 25, 1948. Occurring regularly after about May 6.

LATEST FALL DATE—October 21, 1930.

Breeding birds probably leave by or before the end of August; however, migrants regularly pass through the region during September and into the first week of October.

HABITAT AND DISTRIBUTION — In open second-growth woods, old orchards, scrubby fields, along streams, and in low, moist brushy areas throughout the region.

NESTING—A flimsy platform of twigs and rootlets, located 4 to 8 feet from the ground on the horizontal branch of a tree, though sometimes in thickets or dense bushes. Generally 3 or 4 eggs. June 1, nest with 2 eggs in small thorn tree about 4 feet from ground. June 7, adults gathering nesting material. June 17, female incubating 2 eggs in blackberry tangle. June 20, 4 eggs in nest in viburnum about 6 feet up. June 22, female on nest 6 feet up in small maple tree, 2 eggs.

BLACK-BILLED CUCKOO—Coccyzus erythropthalmus (Wilson)

STATUS—Common migrant; common summer resident.

EARLIEST SPRING DATE—April 25, 1948. Occurring regularly after about May 6.

LATEST FALL DATE—October 29, 1941.

Migrant birds pass through this region throughout the month of September, and there are a few scattered records for the first

10 days of October, but the breeding birds undoubtedly depart much earlier—possibly even in late August.

HABITAT AND DISTRIBUTION — Found throughout the region in the same areas where the yellow-billed cuckoo occurs.

NESTING—Placed 2 to 4 feet from the ground on a horizontal branch of a small tree or shrub, the nest is a shallow saucer of twigs with a finer lining. Two or three eggs is the usual complement. May 19, nest containing 2 eggs, in thorn scrub 4 feet from ground; May 26, 4 eggs; June 2, 1 egg hatched. May 29, nest in wild apple tree, bird incubating 4 eggs. June 11, 3 young in nest in young pine about 4 feet from ground. July 23-29, adult incubating 2 eggs. One instance of a black-billed cuckoo's egg in a robin's nest was reported June 11, 1944. Nests of both birds were in the same small pine tree.

Order STRIGIFORMES

Family TYTONIDAE (Barn Owls)

AMERICAN BARN OWL—Tyto alba pratincola (Bonaparte)

STATUS—Not uncommon permanent resident.

In 1858 Kirkpatrick (1859:373) wrote of the barn owl: "Will probably be found resident in Ohio, but as yet we do not know of a specimen being seen within its limits." Since that time it has become not uncommon in our region. It is so completely nocturnal in its habits that it undoubtedly escapes the sight of most observers and thus may be more numerous than would appear from the limited number of records which we have.

HABITAT AND DISTRIBUTION—Although this species is primarily a bird of the open country, it is most often observed in and about the habitations of man, particularly about barns, silos, and granaries in the country, and about church steeples, water towers, and old abandoned houses in villages and cities.

NESTING—Not confined to any specific type of site, this owl may nest in hollow trees, holes in cliffs, dovecotes, or in any of the structures mentioned above. 1933, Painesville, 4 young raised in spire of church. June 12, Rocky River Valley, 4 young taken from nest in downy stage. July 22, 2 downy young taken from silo on farm. Known to nest under Hilliard Road Bridge in

Rocky River. June 1942, nest with young in shale cliff in Rocky River. April 21, 25, May 3, 1949, eggs laid on these dates in oat bin in barn; only 2 eggs hatched. November 18, 1949, nest in base of water tower on top of building at 2250 Euclid Avenue, adult with 2 downy young apparently about 3 weeks old; since incubation period averages 23 days, the eggs may have been laid as late as October 5.

Family STRIGIDAE (Typical Owls)

EASTERN SCREECH OWL—Otus asio naevius (Gmelin)

STATUS—Common permanent resident.

HABITAT AND DISTRIBUTION—A bird of the orchards, open woods, city parks, and the wooded suburbs.

NESTING—In natural cavities in trees, hollow stumps, deserted woodpecker holes, or in birdhouses, at a height of a few feet to as much as 80 feet. Normally 4 or 5 eggs (one record of 6). April 6, nest and eggs. April 21, nest of 4 eggs. May 12, 4 downy young in nest at base of hollow tree. May 16, 4 young in transition from gray down stage. June 17, nest with 6 young. July 2, 3 well developed young, but still in downy plumage, spent the day in small apple tree in yard on Yellowstone Road, Cleveland Heights. July 10, nest in hollow tree, 4 young.

GREAT HORNED OWL—Bubo virginianus virginianus (Gmelin)

STATUS—Not uncommon permanent resident.

HABITAT AND DISTRIBUTION—This species is principally a bird of the deep woods, swamps, and river bottoms, although, especially during the winter, it sometimes ventures into more open areas.

NESTING—An old nest of the red-tailed or the red-shouldered hawk is the most frequent choice of this owl, which begins nesting early in February. The nests of crows, herons, eagles, and squirrels are also used, and occasionally this owl may utilize a cavity in a tree or a rocky ledge. February 12, Chesterland, bird on nest. February 25-27, Strongsville, 2 eggs hatched. March 8, 9, Willoughby, young hatched; April 23, young left nest. March 31, Waite Hill, one young, two-thirds grown, in nest. April 14, Old Portage (north of Akron), two banded in nest. April 24,

Rocky River, one young just out of nest. In the spring of 1941 a pair raised 2 young in Bedford Metropolitan Park Reservation (April 9, 2 young).

SNOWY OWL—Nyctea scandiaca (Linnaeus)

STATUS—Uncommon and irregular winter visitor.

EARLIEST FALL DATE—November 3, 1946.

LATEST SPRING DATE—April 4, 1935.

Kirkpatrick (1859:382) said of this bird: "Very common during the winter along the lake shore. In the winter of 1858-59 a great many were shot in the neighborhood of Cleveland, and this is the case almost every year."

Apparently as a result of the periodic fluctuation in the population of Arctic hares and lemmings upon which it feeds in its northerly haunts, this "white owl" appears in this region in considerable numbers about every four years. The winter of 1941-42 saw such a flight of these birds, it being estimated that from 100 to 150 reached our region that winter. Again in the winter of 1945-46 there were many records of this species, especially along the lakefront, where it seems to occur most frequently. It was observed at both Gordon and Edgewater Parks, Richmond Beach, and Fairport Harbor, and at the Willoughby Airport. Occasional birds may appear during the winter months even in an "off" year.

AMERICAN HAWK OWL—Surnia ulula caparoch (Müller)

STATUS—Rare winter visitor.

We have the following 3 records of this bird in our region. November 10, 1927, one collected in Pepper Pike Village by Rudolph J. Kula (skin in CMNH collection). December 5, 1940, one reported by B. P. Bole, Jr., seen at Holden Arboretum. December 24, 1940, and again on January 1 and 6, 1941, one reported seen (probably same bird) at Northfield by Rudolph J. Kula.

NORTHERN BARRED OWL—Strix varia varia Barton

STATUS—Common permanent resident.

HABITAT AND DISTRIBUTION—Wooded swamps and dark, secluded beech woods are the usual haunts of this species, which may be found in such areas as Little Mountain, Black Brook, Solon Bog, Rocky River, and the North and South Chagrin Metropolitan Park Reservations.

NESTING—Inept at building its own nest, this owl seems to prefer a cavity in a tree as its nest site, though it frequently appropriates old nests of squirrels, hawks, and crows in which to lay its 2 or 3 eggs. April 16, Elyria, nest in dead stub, entrance hole 10 feet up, 2 heavily incubated eggs. April 18, North Chagrin, 3 young about 2 weeks old in hollow top of beech tree; April 23, 1 young out of nest, 2 young in nest. May 6, North Chagrin, old bird carrying shrew to 2 young in nest. May 8, Rocky River, adult with 3 young.

GREAT GRAY OWL—Strix nebulosa nebulosa Forster

STATUS—Rare and accidental visitor.

Kirkpatrick (1858b) adds this bird to our state list "in consequence of an owl answering the description of this species, having been shot some years ago at Huntsburgh, Geauga County."

LONG-EARED OWL—Asio otus wilsonianus (Lesson)

STATUS—Rare migrant.

Of the 18 records which we have from the Cleveland region for this more northerly breeding woodland owl, 4 are in April; 1, May 18; 1, July 10; 1, September 20; 7, November 1 to 28; 3, December; 1, January 30.

This bird is so nocturnal in its feeding habits, and keeps itself so well concealed during the daytime, that it may easily have escaped notice and may occur here more frequently than the few records indicate. There are 12 specimens from our region in the CMNH collections.

HABITAT AND DISTRIBUTION — Usually found in dense thickets or dark clumps of evergreen trees. Quite in contrast, one bird was observed perched on an iron post 12 inches from the ground at the entrance to the CMNH Auditorium in downtown Cleveland December 19, 1944. Records indicate wide distribution throughout the region.

SHORT-EARED OWL—Asio flammeus flammeus (Pontoppidan)

STATUS—Uncommon migrant; possible rare summer resident.

Of the 33 individuals reported in the period 1917 through 1947, 14 were observed in November and December and 9 in March and April.

HABITAT AND DISTRIBUTION—Unlike most of its relatives, this owl keeps to open country—marshes, grassy fields, and upland pastures—where it seeks out its mousy prey in broad daylight. The few records from the region are for such localities as Mentor Headlands, Pepper Pike Village and Willoughby.

NESTING—On the ground in open low areas.

Ralph A. O'Reilly, Jr. reported a pair frequently seen during the day over an open field near the corner of SOM Center and Cedar Roads, Village of Pepper Pike, during the summer of 1939. Another pair was reported in a similar location near Sulgrave Road, Shaker Heights, from April through July 1939 by Charles H. Knight.

SAW-WHET OWL—Aegolius acadicus acadicus (Gmelin)

STATUS—Uncommon permanent resident.

Although we have 34 relatively recent records of the saw-whet owl in our region, comparatively little seems to be known about the status of the bird here. The records are well distributed throughout the year, and 2 birds in juvenile plumage have been found here.

An interesting fact is that 3 specimens (2 alive, 1 dead) have been picked up in essentially the same neighborhood within the limits of the City of Cleveland (November 1, 1942, one captured alive on a fire escape at 1249 East 23rd Street; October 24, 1945, one picked up dead at 745 East 82nd Street; June 22, 1946, a juvenile captured alive at St. Clair Avenue and East 65th Street. The latter two localities are not far from Gordon Park). Other locations than the City of Cleveland from which the bird has been reported in our region are Chesterland, Holden Arboretum, Willoughby, Gates Mills, Chagrin Falls, Novelty, Waite Hill, Northfield, Freedom Station, Solon, Cleveland Heights, East Cleveland, Medina, Berea, North Olmsted, Lakewood, Bay Village.

HABITAT AND DISTRIBUTION—Essentially a bird of the deep woods, this owl may wander considerably in fall and winter. It is of such a retiring disposition in the daytime that its presence is often unsuspected.

NESTING—In old woodpecker holes or nest boxes. There is no definite nesting record as yet from the region, but the evidence seems to indicate that the species does nest here.

Order CAPRIMULGIFORMES

Family CAPRIMULGIDAE (Goatsuckers)

EASTERN WHIP-POOR-WILL—Caprimulgus vociferus vociferus Wilson

STATUS—Uncommon migrant; uncommon summer resident.

EARLIEST SPRING DATE—April 18, 1948. AVERAGE—May 5. Generally present after about April 25.

LATEST FALL DATE—October 17, 1937.

Breeding birds probably depart by or before the end of August, but there are a few scattered records of migrant birds in September and October.

HABITAT AND DISTRIBUTION—A bird of open woodlands and of the wooded borders of pastures and upland fields. During the spring migration this species is not infrequently heard and seen in metropolitan Cleveland and the suburbs, but the breeding birds occur away from the city in such localities as Little Mountain, Gates Mills, and North Amherst.

NESTING—The 2 eggs are laid on the ground, customarily near the edge of the woods where the undergrowth is sparse. One pair nested at Little Mountain in 1938 in an upland pine-hemlock-red maple forest. In 1940, one pair nested in second growth mixed deciduous woodland in Middleburgh Heights. Several pairs are present regularly throughout the breeding season in the long abandoned quarry section near North Amherst. Nesting dates here are: May 18, 1938, 2 eggs. May 26, 1942, 2 eggs.

EASTERN NIGHTHAWK—Chordeiles minor minor (Forster)

STATUS—Common migrant; common summer resident.

EARLIEST SPRING DATE—March 14, 1922. AVERAGE—April 4. Generally present in some numbers after about May 7.

LATEST FALL DATE—October 12, 1935. Breeding birds depart by the last week in August, but large flights of migrants, as well as scattered individuals, pass through the region in September, chiefly during the first two weeks.

HABITAT AND DISTRIBUTION—Although originally a bird of the open country, the nighthawk has taken to city life in recent times, particularly since the introduction of flat, graveled roofs, and in this region is probably observed most frequently in the metropolitan and suburban, rather than the rural, areas. It even occurs as a breeding bird in the heart of downtown Cleveland.

NESTING—This bird builds no nest, but lays its 2 eggs on the graveled roofs of buildings in the city, and on barren, stony soil or sparsely grown wasteland in rural regions. July 5, 2 eggs on roof of building; July 10, 2 young. July 13, 14, Rocky River, second set of eggs laid on roof of theater; August 2, eggs hatched; August 19, both young flew. July 5, 2 young on roof of apartment in Cleveland Heights. July 21, 2 eggs on roof of building at East 46th and Prospect, Cleveland.

SENNETT'S NIGHTHAWK—Chordeiles minor sennettii Coues

STATUS—Uncommon fall migrant.

Two specimens of this breeding form of the Great Plains region have been collected from migrating flocks of nighthawks at Parma Heights: August 31, 1934, a male; and September 4, 1935, a female. Identification made by J. W. Aldrich and H. C. Oberholser (Aldrich 1936c).

Order APODIFORMES
Family APODIDAE (Swifts)
CHIMNEY SWIFT—Chaetura pelagica (Linnaeus)

STATUS—Common migrant; common summer resident.

EARLIEST SPRING DATE—April 6, 1946. AVERAGE—April 23.

LATEST FALL DATE—October 23, 1937. AVERAGE—October 12.

Large movements of swifts are reported for August 24, 1948, and September 15, 1943.

HABITAT AND DISTRIBUTION—The chimney swift is practically always seen in the air. Its erratic flight and cigar-shaped body make identification easy. Sometimes in the autumn, during migration, flocks may be seen spiralling into chimneys where they roost for the night. It is well distributed over the entire region.

NESTING—Formerly a nester in hollow trees, this swift now chooses chimneys for its nesting site. The nest is made of twigs glued together to form a shallow saucer, attached to the inside of the chimney. While there are many nesting records for this region, there are few detailed observations available.

The following information is furnished by Dr. Ralph W. Dexter, of Kent State University, who is making an intensive study of the life history of this species: "Chimney swifts arrive at Kent between April 22 and April 25. Nest building begins the first week in June usually and requires about three days for construction. Eggs are laid as soon as possible after the nest is completed, one egg laid each day as a rule, but occasionally two days elapse between successive layings, until an average of four eggs are deposited. Both sexes incubate and share equally in caring for the young. Hatching begins three weeks after the eggs are laid, and the eggs hatch a day or two apart. Blue pin feathers appear in two or three days, which break out into black feathers about a week or ten days after hatching. Young leave the nest three or four days after getting the full juvenile plumage."

Dr. S. C. Kendeigh, of the University of Illinois, sends records of a chimney swift's nest observed in the chimney of a sugar house at Gates Mills in 1925, 1932, 1938, and 1939. These indicate that the nest is usually completed by the middle of June, eggs are laid at the rate of 1 daily to a total of 3 or 4, incubation begins at once, young leave chimney second week in August.

An earlier date for young leaving nest is June 20, 1949 (Shankland).

Family TROCHILIDAE (Hummingbirds)

RUBY-THROATED HUMMINGBIRD—Archilochus colubris (Linnaeus)

STATUS—Common migrant; common summer resident.

EARLIEST SPRING DATE—April 25, 1937. AVERAGE—May 11.

84

Latest fall date—October 27, 1945. Average—September 30.

Habitat and Distribution—Well distributed throughout the region wherever there are trees. The hummingbird is not a forest dweller, but is found about woods edges, gardens and open spaces.

Nesting—Nest in small or large trees, 6 to 30 feet up, often on a branch overhanging a path or a pond. Nest saddled on limb, constructed of plant down and decorated with lichens. Eggs usually 2. Many nesting records for the region. Earliest, May 24, bird gathering nesting materials; June 1, apparently incubating. A complete, though late record is the following: July 10, nest completed; July 13-14, eggs laid; July 25, eggs hatched; August 7, young left nest. Another late record is: July 21, first egg laid; July 23 or 24, second egg laid; August 30, young left nest.

Order CORACIIFORMES

Family ALCEDINIDAE (Kingfishers)

EASTERN BELTED KINGFISHER—Megaceryle alcyon alcyon (Linnaeus)

Status—Common migrant; common summer resident.

A few individuals regularly winter here.

Earliest spring date—March 3, 1946. Average—March 18.

Latest fall date—There are many November and December records, and a considerably lesser number in January and February.

Habitat and Distribution — Margins of lakes, ponds and streams. Most numerous along the Lake Erie shore and the courses of the Chagrin, Cuyahoga, Rocky, and Black Rivers, but also frequents small inland ponds and lakes.

Nesting—In holes excavated in the banks of streams or lakes near the top. While there are numerous records of the bird's nesting in the region, there are few detailed observations. One reported from Chardon May 20, 5 eggs. Another reported near the mouth of the Chagrin River June 29 was in a hole in the river bank only 18 inches deep, containing 6 young about 10 days old.

Order PICIFORMES

Family PICIDAE (Woodpeckers)

NORTHERN FLICKER—Colaptes auratus luteus Bangs

STATUS—Common migrant; common summer resident.

EARLIEST SPRING DATE—March 1, 1910. AVERAGE—March 16.

LATEST FALL DATE (Average of last October and November dates) —November 9.

At least one flicker has usually been recorded on Christmas Bird Counts. There are many January and February records.

HABITAT AND DISTRIBUTION—This woodpecker is not usually found in deep woods. More to its liking are the open spaces of parks, orchards, farmlands and suburban residence sections. Well distributed throughout the region.

NESTING—In holes excavated in dead limbs or stubs. Sometimes in nesting boxes, or in old holes of flicker or pileated woodpecker. From a study of many nesting records it appears that nesting preparations usually begin about May 1. Incubation starts about May 15. Young birds appear at entrance June 15. Young are being fed out of nest June 29. Later dates indicate delayed nestings or second broods.

BOREAL FLICKER—Colaptes auratus borealis Ridgway

STATUS—Rare migrant.

There are 2 specimens of this more northerly race of the flicker in the collections of the CMNH taken in our region: a male taken at Everett in Summit County October 13, 1930; a female taken in Cleveland May 26, 1932.

NORTHERN PILEATED WOODPECKER—Dryocopus pileatus abieticola (Bangs)

STATUS—Not uncommon permanent resident.

Mentioned by Kirtland (1850) among species common to Cleveland at the time of the "first surveys" (1796). Twenty-five years ago this bird was thought to be a vanishing species in our region. With better protection, and due in some measure to the refuges afforded by the Cleveland Metropolitan Park System which assures an undisturbed and suitable habitat, it has been increasing in numbers until it is now not uncommon.

HABITAT AND DISTRIBUTION—With us, this woodpecker is to be found in the "big woods", largely in the reservations of the Cleveland Metropolitan Park System, or in the beech-maple-hemlock forests of the Chagrin River drainage, including Little Mountain and the Holden Arboretum.

NESTING—In holes excavated usually in dead stubs. A typical nesting record is the following: April 6, new nesting hole observed; April 13, 27, male seen entering nesting hole; May 4, 11, 18, 25, male and female observed visiting nest; June 1, male and female observed entering nesting hole, sounds indicate feeding of young birds; June 8, male and female observed feeding 3 young; June 10, male and female feeding 3 nearly grown young. Another record is the following: May 23, nest hole in top of dead beech 55 feet up, young heard clamoring inside; May 26, 2 young (male and female) observed with heads out of hole; May 29, adults apparently trying to get young to leave nest; May 29, young male left nest; June 1, young female left nest.

WESTERN RED-BELLIED WOODPECKER—Centurus carolinus zebra (Boddaert)

STATUS—Uncommon permanent resident.

HABITAT AND DISTRIBUTION—From many breeding bird population studies made in the region over a period of years, it appears that this bird, as a breeding species, is here largely restricted to beech-maple woodlands. Only in such an environment has it been reported nesting here. At North Chagrin (65 acres), Holden Arboretum (39 acres), and Wellington just outside our region to the southwest (14 acres), from 1 to 2 pairs are usually (though not always) reported breeding.

Never seen in numbers, it seems to be widely distributed over the region to the east and south, and is particularly likely to be found throughout the beech-maple forests of the Chagrin River watershed. During the winter it may appear in more open country, and then often patronizes feeding stations.

NESTING—In cavities excavated in trees, usually in dead limbs from 20 to 100 feet up. We have no detailed observations of nesting behaviour.

EASTERN RED-HEADED WOODPECKER—Melanerpes erythrocephalus erythrocephalus (Linnaeus)

STATUS—Not uncommon migrant; not uncommon summer resident.

Occasional in winter. Numbers apparently becoming reduced in our region.

EARLIEST SPRING DATE—March 1, 1942. AVERAGE—March 26.

LATEST FALL DATE—December 20, 1941.

There are numerous December records. There are January records for 1922, 1946, and 1948; and February records for 1924, 1938 and 1948. These wintering birds may possibly be migrants from farther north, or their stay may be determined by abundance of beech nuts or pin oak acorns, upon which they feed.

HABITAT AND DISTRIBUTION — This woodpecker is not a forest bird, but is found in more open country, such as parks and woodlots about farm buildings and along roadsides. It is often seen perched on fence posts, telephone poles or isolated dead stubs. More common westerly in our region than easterly.

NESTING—In holes excavated in dead limbs or stubs. Nest building begins as early as May 3. Young birds are visible at nest entrance last 2 weeks of June. Adults have been reported feeding young outside of nest as late as July 15 and August 22. Pairs regularly nest in Lakewood Park, Gordon Park, Wade Park, and Forest Hill Park.

YELLOW-BELLIED SAPSUCKER—Sphyrapicus varius varius (Linnaeus)

STATUS—Common migrant.

EARLIEST SPRING DATE—March 6, 1949. AVERAGE—March 22. Most numerous in April. LATEST—May 23, 1943. AVERAGE—May 9.

EARLIEST FALL DATE—August 15, 1936. AVERAGE—September 25.

Most numerous in October. LATEST—November 5, 1934. AVERAGE—October 12.

Late records are December 18, 1946; December 23, 1931; January 8, 1947; and February 3, 1946, the latter a wintering individual at Waite Hill. During the winter of 1947-48 there were records of single individuals from December 27 to February 22.

HABITAT AND DISTRIBUTION—On migration may be found almost anywhere where there are trees, including forest areas, open woodlands, orchards or city streets.

EASTERN HAIRY WOODPECKER—Dendrocopos villosus villosus (Linnaeus)

STATUS—Not uncommon permanent resident.

Christmas Bird Counts conducted by the Kirtland Bird Club in an area of 15 miles diameter east of Cleveland have listed from 10 to 15 hairy woodpeckers annually for the years 1943 to 1948.

HABITAT AND DISTRIBUTION—This is a bird of the woodlands, although occasionally seen in suburban residence communities or city parks. Well distributed throughout the region wherever woodlands occur.

NESTING—In holes excavated in dead or living trees. April 17, bird drilling nesting hole in small sycamore 15 feet up; April 30, 4 eggs. March 28, new hole 60 feet up in beech; May 22, young coming to entrance; May 30, young still in nest. April 17, excavating hole in sugar maple 75 feet up on under side of ascending living limb; May 29, young noisy in nest; June 19, young still in nest.

NORTHERN DOWNY WOODPECKER — Dendrocopos pubescens medianus (Swainson)

STATUS—Common permanent resident.

Its abundance may be inferred from the fact that during a well organized Christmas Bird Count conducted by the Kirtland Bird Club on January 2, 1949, covering a territory east of Cleveland limited to a 15 mile diameter, no less than 90 downy woodpeckers were counted.

HABITAT AND DISTRIBUTION—Found in all of the forest types of the region as well as in old orchards, second growth woodlands, and about shade trees along roadsides in suburban communities. Regularly patronizes feeding stations in winter.

NESTING—Nests in holes which it excavates in stubs or dead limbs 5 to 50 feet from the ground. May 11, male carrying food to nesting hole. May 16, nest, 4 eggs. May 27, nest in hole 5½ feet from ground, young in nest very noisy. May 30, nest in stub 12 feet up, young in nest, but gone June 2. June 22, 2 young out of nest being fed by adults. August 27, adults feeding 2 young out of nest.

ARCTIC THREE-TOED WOODPECKER — Picoides arcticus (Swainson)

STATUS—Rare and accidental visitor.

This northern species is reported by Baird, Brewer, and Ridgway (1874:531) as having been found as far south as Ohio. Jones (1903:113) says the specimen reported by Brewer above was taken at Akron, Summit County. Jones also reports that Oberlin College has a specimen of this species collected and mounted at Ravenna, Portage County, by John C. Catlin. More recent reports are the following: October 31, 1918, a male bird seen near Painesville (Doolittle 1918:118); March 10, 1940, a male and a female seen on the east branch of the Chagrin River near Chardon by Ruth Eisle and Winifred Goodsell.

Order PASSERIFORMES

Family TYRANNIDAE (Tyrant Flycatchers)

EASTERN KINGBIRD—Tyrannus tyrannus (Linnaeus)

STATUS—Common migrant; common summer resident.

EARLIEST SPRING DATE—April 6, 1948. AVERAGE—April 25.

LATEST FALL DATE—October 4, 1936. AVERAGE—September 20.

HABITAT AND DISTRIBUTION—In open country, old orchards, scrubby fields, and borders of swamps and marshes. Breeding records from Solon, Aurora, Cuyahoga Heights, Fairport, Maple Heights, Little Mountain. Well distributed over the region.

NESTING—The nest is often conspicuously placed, usually in a small tree or shrub, or even on a telegraph pole, from 5 to 20 feet from the ground. June 2, nest, 3 eggs; June 18, 2 young three to four days old; June 28, 2 young out of nest. June 20, nest, 3 eggs. July 13, nest, 3 young. July 13 and August 15, young being fed out of nest.

ARKANSAS KINGBIRD—Tyrannus verticalis Say

STATUS—Rare and accidental migrant.

One bird of this species was reported seen on the grounds adjoining the CMNH in downtown Cleveland June 1, 1945. Observed for about 10 minutes at close range by A. B. Williams.

NORTHERN CRESTED FLYCATCHER—Myiarchus crinitus boreus Bangs

STATUS—Common migrant; common summer resident.

EARLIEST SPRING DATE—April 17, 1938. AVERAGE—April 30.

LATEST FALL DATE—October 6, 1946.

HABITAT AND DISTRIBUTION—A bird of the woodlands, though occasionally seen in suburban residence sections. Well distributed over the region in such places, but nowhere abundant.

NESTING—In holes in trees, either old woodpecker holes or natural cavities. May 23, old bird observed entering hole with nesting material (cast snake skin). June 27, birds carrying nesting material into hole in telegraph pole, snake skin dangling from entrance. July 2, 3 young following 2 adults begging for food. August 14, 2 young out of nest being fed by adults.

EASTERN PHOEBE—Sayornis phoebe (Latham)

STATUS—Common migrant; common summer resident.

EARLIEST SPRING DATE—March 2, 1929. AVERAGE—March 10.

LATEST FALL DATE—November 30, 1933. AVERAGE—October 20.

HABITAT AND DISTRIBUTION—This flycatcher is usually found in woodlands or in open farming country wherever its favorite nesting sites are available. Widely distributed throughout the region.

NESTING—Nests commonly on beams or supports under bridges, ledges in caves, or on the face of rock cliffs, projections on buildings or over doors, or (frequently in forests) under the tangled roots of some large overturned tree. From a study of many nesting records, it appears that the earliest nest building recorded here is March 29. Peak of nest building activity April 17-26. Latest, May 30. First egg, April 18. Average, April 23. Latest eggs, July 18. First young, May 19. Latest young in nest, July 17.

YELLOW-BELLIED FLYCATCHER—Empidonax flaviventris
(W. M. and S. F. Baird)

STATUS—Uncommon migrant.

EARLIEST SPRING DATE—May 3, 1937. PEAK OF NUMBERS — May 9-30. LATEST—June 27, 1938.

EARLIEST FALL DATE—August 24, 1940. LATEST — September 26, 1934.

HABITAT AND DISTRIBUTION—On migration reported from such varied locations as Burton, Middlefield, Little Mountain, Richmond, North Chagrin, Gordon Park, Shaker Lakes, Parma, North Olmsted, Lakewood, Rocky River, Avon and downtown Cleveland.

ACADIAN FLYCATCHER—Empidonax virescens (Vieillot)

STATUS—Common migrant; locally common summer resident.

EARLIEST SPRING DATE—May 2, 1880, 1936 and 1948. AVERAGE— May 10. PEAK OF NUMBERS—May 12-18.

LATEST FALL DATE—October 8, 1937. AVERAGE—September 14.

HABITAT AND DISTRIBUTION—This flycatcher prefers moist woodlands including shady glens and ravines. Its abundance in an optimum habitat may be inferred from the fact that in a 15-year study of the breeding bird population of a 65-acre tract of beech-maple forest at North Chagrin, Arthur B. Williams found an average of 3.2 pairs nesting annually from 1932 to 1947. Numbers during this period varied from 2 pairs in 1935 to 8 pairs in 1941. In a similar study conducted in a 50-acre tract of oak-hickory ridge and beech-maple slope, Harold E. Wallin found 2 pairs nesting in 1946 and in 1947. In another similar study in a 30-acre tract of wet beech-maple woodland, Vera Carrothers and Margarette E. Morse found 4 pairs nesting in 1942. Breeding records also reported from Elyria, North Akron, Hinckley, Holden Arboretum, Little Mountain, Fairview.

NESTING—Nest often, perhaps usually, suspended from a crotch or between parallel twigs near the end of a drooping limb of a beech tree overhanging a small stream bed or ravine, perhaps 15 feet from the ground. Eggs usually 3. From a study of numerous nesting records it appears that the nest is usually completed the first week in June; incubation may be in process from about June 10 to July 2; young being fed in nest June 20.

92

ALDER TRAILL'S FLYCATCHER—Empidonax traillii traillii Brewster

STATUS—Common migrant; locally common summer resident.

EARLIEST SPRING DATE—May 2, 1942 and 1948. AVERAGE—May 7.

LATEST FALL DATE—October 16, 1944.

Apparently rare in the region a century ago, since Read (1853a:395) mentions it only as reported "on good authority" as having been seen in the neighborhood of Cleveland. Kirtland (1874a:170) says, however, that it was seen repeatedly prior to 1852.

HABITAT AND DISTRIBUTION—Prefers marshy or wet locations with thorns or other scrubby growth. Also found in wet meadows overgrown with brambles or in the near neighborhood of streams. Its abundance in an optimum habitat may be inferred from the fact that in a 5-year study (1943-1947) of a 15.3-acre tract, including small pond and border of briers, thorns and small trees, Vera Carrothers found an average of 7 pairs nesting annually. During this period numbers of nesting pairs varied from 3 to 11. Well distributed throughout the region in favorable locations.

NESTING—Nest is usually placed from 4 to 10 feet from the ground in brambles, shrubs or small trees. Earliest nesting record is May 27, when a bird was observed on nest incubating 2 eggs. From numerous records it appears that the height of incubation period is June 15 to 30. Young are usually found in the nest July 3 to 20. Latest date for young in the nest is August 3. Number of eggs 2 to 4. Incubation period 14 days. Young in nest 13 to 14 days.

LEAST FLYCATCHER—Empidonax minimus (W. M. and S. F. Baird)

STATUS—Common migrant; possible rare summer resident.

EARLIEST SPRING DATE—April 17, 1924. AVERAGE—May 3. There are enough June, July and August records to indicate a small summer resident population.

LATEST FALL DATE—October 11, 1948.

HABITAT AND DISTRIBUTION—During migration may be found in many open situations, such as woodlands, old orchards, suburban residence sections, edges of swamps or streams. Annually during migration it appears in some numbers on the grounds of the CMNH in downtown Cleveland from May 11 to 28. Reported from all sections of the region first two weeks in May, when heaviest migration movement occurs.

NESTING—Although no actual nests of this species have been reported in the region, summer records of singing males, or pairs, in typical nesting habitats have been reported from Stebbin's Gulch, Little Mountain, Gates Mills, Middleburgh Heights, Auburn, and Rocky River Valley.

EASTERN WOOD PEWEE—Contopus virens (Linnaeus)

STATUS—Common migrant; common summer resident.

EARLIEST SPRING DATE—March 12, 1921. AVERAGE — April 22. Common by May 10.

LATEST FALL DATE—October 10, 1943. AVERAGE—September 30.

HABITAT AND DISTRIBUTION—Commonly found in woodlands, though frequently also in suburban communities where there are groups of large trees. Widely distributed throughout the region wherever suitable woodlands occur. The degree of abundance of this species in a favorable habitat may be inferred from the fact that in a 15-year study of the breeding bird population of a 65-acre tract of beech-maple woodland from 1932 to 1947, Arthur B. Williams found an average of 6.4 pairs nesting annually. Numbers varied from 5 pairs in 1936, 1937, 1939, 1940, to 8 pairs in 1946 and 1947.

NESTING — Nest usually saddled on horizontal branch (often a dead one). In a high, closed forest like that at North Chagrin, nests have been noted 50 to 75 feet from the ground. On the other hand, we have in a different environment a record of a nest only 12 feet up. May 14, nest, 5 eggs. May 19, nest, 4 eggs. July 2, nest, 2 eggs. Incubating birds have been observed from June 12 to August 15. Young in the nest have been reported from July 4 to September 1. Latest record of young being fed by old bird September 13. Two broods of one pair have been reported by Herbert Brandt, the first brood consisting of 3 young, the second of 1. This last bird left the nest September 1.

94

OLIVE-SIDED FLYCATCHER—Nuttallornis borealis (Swainson)

STATUS—Uncommon migrant.

EARLIEST SPRING DATE—May 3, 1942. AVERAGE—May 16. LATEST —July 5, 1941.

EARLIEST FALL DATE—August 1, 1938 and 1948. LATEST—October 6, 1946.

HABITAT AND DISTRIBUTION—During migration may be seen almost anywhere, but usually in open country. Records come from Chardon, Holden Arboretum, Little Mountain, North Chagrin, Shaker Lakes, Northfield, Cuyahoga Falls, Aurora, Lakewood, Rocky River, Avon-on-the-Lake.

Family ALAUDIDAE (Larks)

HOYT'S HORNED LARK—Eremophila alpestris hoyti (Bishop)

STATUS—Rare and accidental visitor.

This northwestern race of the horned lark is not distinguishable in the field from *E. a. praticola*. It is possible, therefore, that reports of *praticola* may include some *hoyti*. A specimen of *hoyti* in the collection of the CMNH was taken at Mentor Headlands April 8, 1931.

NORTHERN HORNED LARK—Eremophila alpestris alpestris (Linnaeus)

STATUS—Rare autumn and spring visitor.

This northern race of the horned lark is occasionally reported seen in the midst of flocks of prairie horned larks or snow buntings. Probably the first specimens collected at Cleveland are 2 (females) taken on the Lake Erie shore April 1, 1851, by Kirtland. Skins are in the U. S. National Museum and have been identified by H. C. Oberholser. Other dates are April 8, 18, October 19, 26. We have one winter record, February 2, 1947. In the collection of the CMNH is a specimen labeled April 18, 1885, Cleveland (Baldwin), and 12 specimens from Kipton, Lorain County, just outside our region to the west.

PRAIRIE HORNED LARK—Eremophila alpestris praticola (Henshaw)

STATUS—Not uncommon permanent resident.

HABITAT AND DISTRIBUTION—These birds frequent open, treeless fields, sand dunes along the Lake Erie shore, golf courses, and roadsides in farming country. Usually seen in flocks in the fall and winter numbering from a few birds to as many as 200. Well distributed throughout the region.

NESTING—On the ground among short grasses and weeds in very open treeless situations. Nests often found on golf courses and grassy strips along highways in open country. Nest built in shallow excavation in the soil. A complete record is the following: March 24, bird excavating in fine slag by roadside; interrupted by a severe snow storm; March 31, nest building resumed; May 7, 4 eggs; May 17, 2 eggs hatched; May 18, remaining 2 eggs hatched; May 27, young left nest. An earlier record is that of nest and 3 eggs March 27.

Family HIRUNDINIDAE (Swallows)

TREE SWALLOW—Iridoprocne bicolor (Vieillot)

STATUS—Common migrant; locally common summer resident.
EARLIEST SPRING DATE—March 24, 1948. AVERAGE—April 16.
LATEST FALL DATE—October 2, 1946.

HABITAT AND DISTRIBUTION— Usually seen in the air and about water. Sometimes perches on wires or on dead trees or bushes about water. Well distributed over the region in suitable habitats.

NESTING—Usually in old woodpecker holes in dead trees or stubs about the marshy margins of ponds or lakes. Readily accepts quarters in nest boxes placed on posts standing in water a few feet from shore. May 30, nest in box, 4 eggs. June 14, adults feeding young in nest.

AMERICAN BANK SWALLOW—Riparia riparia riparia (Linnaeus)

STATUS—Common migrant; locally common summer resident.
EARLIEST SPRING DATE—April 3, 1949. AVERAGE—April 20.
LATEST FALL DATE—October 9, 1948. AVERAGE—September 4.

HABITAT AND DISTRIBUTION — Usually seen in the air, often skimming over the surface of ponds or rivers, sometimes perched on the telephone or other wires or on dead branches of trees or shrubs near water. Well distributed over the region in suitable habitats.

NESTING—In holes excavated in sand or gravel banks, along river edges, or road cuts or pits. In such locations many pairs of bank swallows may be nesting in a colony. A colony of 300 to 400 birds reported nesting in a sand bank near Lorain May 31, 1931. Another colony of about 75 birds reported nesting in a gravel quarry near Chardon May 15, 1944, 43 holes about a foot apart counted in 3 strata levels. A pair started excavation in bank on shore of Lake Erie May 9, 1930. A colony of 50 birds nesting in sand bank in road cut, Snowville Road, Brecksville, May 8, 1949.

The following detailed account refers to a small colony of birds observed one mile south of Miles Avenue and East 116th Street, Cleveland: April 19, 1938, 5 pairs nesting in sand bank about 15 feet from the ground. Both sexes excavating. Nest about 20 inches back from entrance. Finished May 30; eggs laid first week in June; young hatched June 16; left nest June 28, 29.

EASTERN ROUGH-WINGED SWALLOW — Stelgidopteryx ruficollis serripennis (Audubon)

STATUS—Common migrant; locally common summer resident.

EARLIEST SPRING DATE—April 6, 1946. AVERAGE—April 18.

LATEST FALL DATE—September 22, 1947. AVERAGE—September 10.

HABITAT AND DISTRIBUTION—Usually seen in the air, often skimming over the surface of ponds or rivers, sometimes perched on telephone or other wires or on dead branches of trees or shrubs near water. Well distributed over the region.

NESTING—In natural holes in banks, along river or stream edges, in crevices in retaining walls, open ends of smaller drainage pipes, or in nooks in shale cliffs, or under bridges. Although we have many reports of the nesting of this species within the region, there are no detailed observations of nest history. June 6, nest, 4 eggs. July 10, adults feeding 5 fledglings perched on telephone wire.

97

BARN SWALLOW–Hirundo rustica erythrogaster Boddaert

STATUS—Common migrant; common summer resident.

EARLIEST SPRING DATE—March 15, 1936. AVERAGE—April 20.

LATEST FALL DATE—October 4, 1941. AVERAGE—September 15.

HABITAT AND DISTRIBUTION—Usually seen on the wing in open farming country skimming over surface of ponds or rivers, or low over meadows. Sometimes perches on wires. Well distributed over the region.

NESTING—On rafters, or other projections, in old barns, garages or outhouses. June 24, nest, 4 eggs. August 10, nest, 5 eggs. Nest construction begun May 29, finished June 5; eggs laid 1 daily to a total of 5; last egg, June 11; incubation began June 11; eggs hatched June 26; young left nest July 12-14.

The following complete account refers to a nest inside a garage in Shaker Heights: May 16, nest construction begun; May 23, building still in progress, both birds working; May 26-30, one egg laid each day, 5 in all; June 11, first egg hatched; June 12, second egg hatched; June 13, third egg hatched; June 14, fourth and fifth eggs hatched; June 26, young out of nest, perched on rafters; June 27, young learning to fly; June 29, young perched on wires ready to care for themselves.

NORTHERN CLIFF SWALLOW–Petrochelidon pyrrhonota pyrrhonota (Vieillot)

STATUS—Uncommon migrant; uncommon summer resident.

EARLIEST SPRING DATE—April 3, 1880. AVERAGE—May 2.

LATEST FALL DATE—September 21, 1941.

HABITAT AND DISTRIBUTION—Usually seen on migration flying low over surface of pond or stream or low over meadows. Reported from both east and west sections of our region.

NESTING—In mud nests constructed on sides of buildings, such as old barns. Usually a number of birds nest together thus as a colony. A few years ago there was a well-known colony nesting year after year on the side of an old barn in Willoughby. The only record of an egg date we have is from a nest in Warrensville, June 13, 1929, 4 eggs. July 3, 1949, 8 nests with young under barn eaves at Novelty.

PURPLE MARTIN—Progne subis subis (Linnaeus)

STATUS—Common migrant; locally common summer resident.

EARLIEST SPRING DATE—March 1, 1929. AVERAGE—April 14.

LATEST FALL DATE—November 11, 1931. AVERAGE—September 13.

HABITAT AND DISTRIBUTION—Usually seen in the air over open country or about "martin houses" which have been erected for its use. Nesting in colonies, it is not a bird of general distribution, but is regularly seen on migration throughout the region. In the fall often large flocks may be seen perched on wires along the roadside. One such flock, estimated at 3000 birds, was reported August 14, 1932, from Lakewood.

NESTING—Now commonly nests in multiple "apartment houses" put up for its occupancy on golf courses, country estates or farm buildings, or even in built-up portions of cities. While we have many records of nesting colonies in the region, there are no detailed observations of nest history. Old birds have been noted feeding young about ready to fly August 14.

Family CORVIDAE (Jays, Magpies, and Crows)

NORTHERN BLUE JAY—Cyanocitta cristata bromia Oberholser

STATUS—Common permanent resident; common migrant.

Migrating flocks are often noted along the Lake Erie shore in spring.

The abundance of this species is indicated by the count of 82 individuals seen during the Christmas Bird Count January 2, 1949, which covered a territory of 15 miles in diameter east of Cleveland.

HABITAT AND DISTRIBUTION—Prefers wooded country or territory of scattered trees and dense undergrowth. Generally distributed and perhaps most evident in wooded residential areas, particularly where there is an abundance of oak and beech trees, the mast of which is a favorite food of the jay.

NESTING—March 15, nest construction begun on base of old nest occupied in the two previous years (identical site); nest completed and 5 eggs laid. April 7, nest begun; April 12, nest completed; April 16, first egg; April 23, 5 eggs; May 7, eggs hatched. April 20-25, jays took nest away from robin; April 25, jay sitting on nest. May 10, nest in swamp forest near edge 12 feet up; May 17, 4 eggs. May 27, 28, 30, bird incubating in nest 7 feet up. June 10, nest with 4 eggs in pine. June 7-16, adults feeding young in nest; June 17, young left nest.

NORTHERN RAVEN—Corvus corax principalis Ridgway

STATUS—Formerly not uncommon, now absent from the region.

Wilson (1828:167) wrote of the raven: ''On the lakes, and particularly in the neighborhood of the Falls of the river Niagara, they are numerous; and it is a remarkable fact, that where they so abound, the Common Crow, *C. corone*, seldom makes its appearance.''

Kirtland (1850) mentions the raven as among the birds common to Cleveland at the time of the ''first surveys'' (1796). Two years later it was noted as ''not so numerous as they once were, but still frequently seen'' (Read 1853a:327).

There are no recent authoritative records for the raven in our region. The species is now largely restricted to more northerly latitudes or to the higher parts of the Appalachians.

EASTERN CROW—Corvus brachyrhynchos brachyrhynchos Brehm

STATUS—Common migrant; common summer resident; more or less regular in reduced numbers in winter.

While it is difficult to give definite early and late dates of migration, crows usually appear here in numbers in the latter part of February. By early March large flocks have arrived. Such a flock, noted in migration along the Lake Erie shore February 28, 1931, was estimated at over 10,000. On March 22, 1931, flocks estimated at 330 and 500 were noted.

The autumn migration is not so obvious. Numbers gradually decrease during November and December. A migration movement of ''several thousand'' crows was reported November 25, 1937, near Akron. These birds were traveling at so great a height that they were invisible to the naked eye, but plainly seen with binoculars (J. E. Lieftinck).

Winter roosts of crows have been reported at various times in Cleveland Heights, East Cleveland, and Barberton.

HABITAT AND DISTRIBUTION—During summer prefers woods and groves in the vicinity of farms and open country. Often seen on the Lake Erie shore.

NESTING—Commonly in trees 50 or more feet from the ground. March 25, nest building begun. April 23, nest, 5 eggs. May 1, nest 15 feet up in tupelo on horizontal branch, 3 downy young with eyes not yet open; May 21, young almost fully feathered. June 17, nest, 4 young.

Family PARIDAE (Titmice, Verdins, and Bush-tits)

EASTERN BLACK-CAPPED CHICKADEE — Parus atricapillus atricapillus (Linnaeus)

STATUS—Common permanent resident.

The abundance of this species in the region may be inferred from the record of a well-organized Christmas Bird Count, conducted by the Kirtland Bird Club January 2, 1949, when a total of 209 chickadees were reported seen in an area of 15 miles diameter to the east of Cleveland.

HABITAT AND DISTRIBUTION—Found generally over the region during the winter months, but inclined to retire to the forests, open woodlands, and orchards during the breeding season. Regular visitor to feeding stations in winter. In a 65-acre tract of beech-maple-hemlock woodland, Arthur B. Williams in a 16-year study of the breeding birds of the area found an average of 3.2 pairs nesting annually.

NESTING—It nests in tree cavities, holes in posts and in bird boxes provided for its use. Nest may be from 2 to 60 feet above the ground, and is usually lined with fur or hair. March 31, pair carrying nesting material to hole in guard post along park road. April 18, nest under construction in dead apple stub, 10 feet up. May 16, nest of rabbit hair, 8 eggs, in box on post; May 30, 7 eggs hatched. June 19, 22, adults feeding young out of nest.

NORTHERN CAROLINA CHICKADEE—Parus carolinensis extimus (Todd and Sutton)

STATUS—Rare and accidental visitor.

In the CMNH collection are 2 specimens of this northern race of the Carolina chickadee, one taken at Hudson May 1, 1935; and one taken at Aurora Pond May 8, 1935.

TUFTED TITMOUSE—Parus bicolor Linnaeus

STATUS—Common permanent resident.

Its abundance may be inferred from the fact that over a period of 18 years (1931-1948) an average of 22 individuals have been observed annually during Christmas Bird Counts in an area of 15 miles diameter east of Cleveland (minimum for the period, 11; maximum, 87).

HABITAT AND DISTRIBUTION—Most in evidence in the winter and early spring, usually in wooded areas in the rural sections of the region. Also observed along wooded drives, in cemeteries, and residential districts, particularly where beech and oak trees grow.

NESTING—Nests in tree cavities, such as old woodpecker holes, 5-40 feet from the ground. Nesting activities begin in late April or early May. April 27, bird carrying dry leaves gathered on the ground to natural cavity 65 feet up in large beech; May 10, nest complete, no eggs. May 20, 7 eggs. May 2, nest in natural cavity 18 feet up in small beech, 7 eggs. June 27, family of 8 leaving nest.

Family SITTIDAE (Nuthatches)

EASTERN WHITE-BREASTED NUTHATCH—Sitta carolinensis cookei Oberholser

STATUS—Common permanent resident.

The abundance of this species here may be inferred from the fact that in a Christmas Bird Count conducted by the Kirtland Bird Club January 2, 1949, in an area of 15 miles diameter east of Cleveland, 52 of these birds were recorded.

HABITAT AND DISTRIBUTION—Found in most wooded areas, and about large shade trees in suburban residence sections. Regularly patronizes feeding stations in winter. In a breeding bird population study in a 65-acre tract of beech-maple-hemlock, Arthur B. Williams found an average of 3.3 pairs of nuthatches nesting annually over a 16-year period.

NESTING—Nests in cavities in trees, seeming to prefer natural openings in large trees. Nest building usually takes place between April 10 and 20, and the set of eggs is usually completed by the 27th. Same site may be used several years. April 16, bird carry-

102

ing nesting material into hole in beech. April 27, nest in round cavity about 25 feet up in beech, 7 eggs, same site used in previous years. May 1, nest 13 feet up in small white ash, 8 eggs. April 25, nest 35 feet up in beech, 8 eggs. May 7, 2 adults carrying food to young in hole in black walnut 25 feet up. June 14, 4 young perched near hole in sycamore 60 feet up; one adult feeding young. August 15, 2 adults feeding 4 young out of nest.

RED-BREASTED NUTHATCH—Sitta canadensis Linnaeus

STATUS—Common to rare migrant; irregular winter visitor; rare summer resident.

EARLIEST FALL DATE—August 22, 1949.

LATEST SPRING DATE—May 25, 1946.

Although it has been recorded here every month of the year, its times of greatest abundance are in May and December. It often winters here in considerable numbers. In other years it may be rare or not present. There are a few June, July and August records.

HABITAT AND DISTRIBUTION—This is a bird of wooded areas. During migration it may be looked for almost anywhere where there are trees. In winter, if the crop of beech nuts is ample, these birds tend to congregate in beech woods, where the nuts of these trees form a regular part of their diet.

NESTING—In his study of the breeding birds of a 75-acre tract of white pine-hemlock forest on Little Mountain, B. P. Bole, Jr. (1938) found two pairs nesting there in 1938. Another probable nesting record is indicated by the collection of a juvenal female at Mentor Headlands by John H. Dittrick on July 7, 1931 (Aldrich 1934:97).

Family CERTHIIDAE (Creepers)

EASTERN BROWN CREEPER—Certhia familiaris americana Bonaparte

STATUS—Common migrant; rare summer resident; occasionally common in winter.

EARLIEST MARCH DATE—March 3, 1883, 1932 and 1941.

LATEST OCTOBER DATE—October 28, 1938.

We have records of its occurrence here in every month of the year. Most abundant in March and October.

HABITAT AND DISTRIBUTION—Although normally a bird of the woodlands, it may be seen during migration almost anywhere where there are trees. It has been recorded occasionally in downtown Cleveland, and there is one record of a bird of this species observed creeping up the wall of the inner court of Hotel Cleveland, apparently hunting for food.

NESTING—Although Ingersoll (1883:304) lists this species as breeding here, we have but one definite breeding record. On May 4, 1947, at the edge of a swamp forest near Aurora, an adult bird, carrying nesting material into the space behind a loose piece of bark on an elm tree, was observed by Carl F. Hamann. On May 15 two adults similarly engaged were noted. On May 23 there were 3 eggs in the nest. On May 31 the nest was found torn apart and the eggs broken. The nest and remains of egg shells are in the CMNH collections.

Adult brown creepers were also observed June 21 and June 23, 1947, at Aurora; and on July 4, 1947, at Avon.

Family TROGLODYTIDAE (Wrens)

EASTERN HOUSE WREN—Troglodytes aëdon aëdon Vieillot

STATUS—Uncommon migrant.

There is one specimen of this species in the collection of the CMNH, obtained after it had been killed by flying into the tower of the Cleveland Terminal Building May 19, 1933. It was identified by Aldrich (1936a:98), who was of the opinion that this species probably occurs more or less regularly in migration in the eastern part of the state.

OHIO HOUSE WREN—Troglodytes aëdon baldwini Oberholser

STATUS—Common migrant; common summer resident.

EARLIEST SPRING DATE—March 15, 1945. AVERAGE (of 20 April dates)—April 18.

LATEST FALL DATE—November 21, 1943. AVERAGE—October 12.

HABITAT AND DISTRIBUTION—Usually about man's habitation, farmyards, orchards, residential districts. Also woods-borders and roadsides. Anywhere where nesting cavities or houses are available. Generally distributed throughout the region.

NESTING—In natural cavities in trees or fences, under eaves, in bird houses, or even in tin cans or other odd places. This subspecies of the house wren has been intensively studied by Baldwin (1931) (after whom the bird is named) and Kendeigh (1934;1941) at the Baldwin Bird Research Laboratory at Gates Mills, by means of trap nest boxes and numbered bands. Kendeigh concluded from a study of many nesting records that the incubation period for this species is about 13 days, the period from hatching to leaving the nest 15 days, and that the young are cared for out of the nest for another 13 days. One of Baldwin's nesting records is: July 4, nest started; July 6, nest completed; July 13, set of eggs completed; July 26, eggs hatched; August 10, young left nest. This species starts nesting the first or second week in May. There are two nesting periods, one from early May to late June; the other from early July to middle or late August. Eggs, 5-7. Two or three broods. Young in nest as late as August 20. The house wren may change mates for second nestings, and a male may have two females with nests at the same time. The maximum number of pairs nesting in 15 acres from 1921-1933 was 17 and the minimum 7 annually; average for the entire period 9.5.

Other breeding bird studies range from 1 pair in 15 acres at East Claridon in 1937, to 8 pairs in 75 acres at Little Mountain in 1938, and 13 pairs (in boxes) in 43 acres at Holden Arboretum in 1939.

EASTERN WINTER WREN—Troglodytes troglodytes hiemalis Vieillot

STATUS—Not uncommon migrant; not uncommon winter visitor.

EARLIEST FALL DATE—September 15, 1945. AVERAGE (of 10 September dates)—September 24.

LATEST SPRING DATE—May 19, 1946. AVERAGE (of 13 May dates) —May 9.

Regularly recorded September, October, November, December, January. Heaviest migration in months of April and October. There are several summer records: June 23, 1938, Fairport (Akers); June 24, 1948(2), Kent (Dexter); July 2, 5, 23, 1926, one seen in same place in a deep hemlock-fringed ravine near Gates Mills (Kendeigh 1926:347) ; July 4, 1938, a singing male reported from Little Mountain (Bole 1938) ; August 30, 1947(2), Fullerton (Gaede).

HABITAT AND DISTRIBUTION — In winter and on migration, around fallen logs and brush piles, dense undergrowth, deep woods. More generally distributed east and southeast. Many records from North Chagrin, Little Mountain, Shaker Lakes, Mentor-Richmond area, Rocky River Valley.

NESTING—Wheaton (1882:232) in referring to this species says he is "of the opinion that it breeds in Northern Ohio, having taken a young individual in this vicinity September 9th, 1874, in a plumage which indicated that it had left the nest only shortly before." One needs to remember that the remnants of the boreal forest in northern Ohio in 1874 were much more extensive then than now. Also note the more recent summer records given above.

APPALACHIAN BEWICK'S WREN—Thryomanes bewickii altus Aldrich

STATUS—Rare migrant; rare summer resident.

There are 5 occurrences of this species recorded for the Cleveland region: April 8, 1934(1), at Cuyahoga Falls (Baird 1934:183) ; April 18, 1914(1), at Chardon (Cook 1915b) ; April 18, 1943 (2 birds together), at Cuyahoga Falls (Mayfield 1943:8) ; May 16, 1944 (pair nesting), at Kent (Dexter) ; Cleveland, October 24 (no year given—Bent 1948:182).

NESTING—The nesting pair at Kent in 1944 was first noticed the first week in May. Nest discovered May 16 in a yard adjacent to a woodlot, constructed on a broad ledge under the eaves of a well-house. Three eggs were laid, two of which hatched. The young left the nest June 3. June 4, parents feeding young birds in brush and second growth of woodlot. There is also a nesting record for this species May 26, 1933, at Berlin Heights, just outside our region to the southwest.

NORTHERN CAROLINA WREN — Thryothorus ludovicianus ludovicianus (Latham)

STATUS—Uncommon permanent resident.

Population as a rule considerably reduced after severe winters.

HABITAT AND DISTRIBUTION—Brush piles, fallen logs, willow thickets near water, in woods or near houses. More commonly recorded in Rocky River Valley, otherwise generally distributed throughout the region in suitable habitats.

NESTING—In natural cavities, under logs or brushwood, in woods or near houses. March 28, nest begun on window ledge of house; March 30, nest complete; no eggs laid. May 11, adults feeding 3 young in nest; May 20, nest empty. May 24, 4 young flying about in bushes with adults. A pair was reported nesting in 1933 in the Rocky River Valley near the Trailside Museum there, and another pair nesting in 1938 near the Trailside Museum in the North Chagrin Metropolitan Park. May 8, 1949, 4 young left nest built under porch roof of building near Ohio Canal, Brecksville.

NORTHEASTERN LONG-BILLED MARSH WREN — Telmatodytes palustris dissaëptus (Bangs)

STATUS—Common migrant; locally common summer resident.

EARLIEST SPRING DATE—April 20, 1938. AVERAGE—May 6.

LATEST FALL DATE—October 21, 1946. AVERAGE—September 27.

HABITAT AND DISTRIBUTION—Marshes and swamps near sluggish streams and ponds. More generally observed east and south—Fairport, Holden Arboretum, Richmond, Cuyahoga Valley, Bedford, Black Brook, North Chagrin Pond, Shaker Lakes. Nesting colonies reported at Aurora Pond, Corning Lake, Richmond, Mentor Marsh, and Abram's Lake. In a study of the breeding bird population of a 15-acre tract of marsh at Aurora Pond, John W. Aldrich found 9 pairs nesting in 1932, 9 pairs in 1933, 7 pairs in 1934, 4 pairs in 1937, 16 pairs in 1938, and 19 pairs in 1939. In a new colony at Corning Lake in 1941, Philip N. Moulthrop reported 7 pairs nesting. At Abram's Lake in 1942, George Bing reported 8 pairs nesting.

NESTING—Nest globular, constructed of reeds, attached to cattails, and built over water. May 29, nest, 2 eggs. June 1, nest, 2 eggs. July 7, second broods started. July 16, nest completed, but not used.

SHORT-BILLED MARSH WREN—Cistothorus platensis stellaris (Naumann)

STATUS—Uncommon migrant; rare summer resident.

EARLIEST SPRING DATE—April 7, 1946. AVERAGE—May 15.

LATEST FALL DATE—October 20, 1928. AVERAGE—September 21.

HABITAT AND DISTRIBUTION—Moist meadows, edges of marshes near streams and ponds, east and southeast. In migration most often observed in marsh areas near Lake Erie in eastern portion of region. Very local in distribution, not constant from year to year.

NESTING—Nest in clump of sedge or marsh grass on or close to the ground. At Aurora Pond 3 pairs nested in a 15-acre tract in 1932. John W. Aldrich located 3 pairs at Bradley Pond, June 14, 1932; a breeding colony of 12 pairs in an extensive meadow of pure sedge and seedbox at Aurora Pond July 8, 1932; 3 singing males in a sedge meadow bordering another marsh area at Aurora Pond July 23, 1932, and nest and recently hatched young in clump of sedge overshadowed by jewelweed and marsh grasses August 20; no birds found in same area in 1933, and only 3 pairs found there in 1934.

Family MIMIDAE (Mockingbirds and Thrashers)

EASTERN MOCKINGBIRD—Mimus polyglottos polyglottos (Linnaeus)

STATUS—Rare and accidental migrant; probably rare permanent resident.

Mentioned by Read (1853a:383) as a rare visitor to the Western Reserve. First reported in the Cleveland Bird Calendar in 1917. Since then 40 occurrences have been reported (1917-1948), and these have been more frequent in recent years. Reported during every month of the year except February and July. Of the 40 records since 1917, 21 were in April and May, 4 in June, 9 in December and January.

Habitat and Distribution—Birds reported have been near homes, in gardens, in open places or thickets in parks. Some are reported as staying in the same vicinity for days or weeks. Records well distributed over the region.

Nesting—Wheaton (1882:210) mentions one pair reported by Dr. John Darby, of Cleveland, as nesting for several years at Rockport (now Lakewood) near Dr. Kirtland's home (previous to 1882). Read (1853a:383) mentions a pair that nested at Tallmadge for several years. We have no recent nesting record.

CATBIRD—Dumetella carolinensis (Linnaeus)

Status—Common migrant; common summer resident.

Earliest spring date—April 3, 1917. Average—April 27.

Latest fall date—November 3, 1934. Average—October 10.

Winter records are December 31, 1944; December 24, 27, 1947, one reported each date.

Habitat and Distribution—Wide range of habitat; landscaped areas, open field and scrub, woods edges, second growth woodlots, banks of rivers and streams, marshes and swamp forests. Generally found where there are dense thickets, often near water. Well distributed throughout the region.

The greatest density of nesting birds reported in breeding bird studies is 12 pairs in 15 acres of farmland and landscaped area, a controlled environment, at the Baldwin Bird Research Laboratory at Gates Mills in 1932, reported by S. C. Kendeigh; and 9 pairs in 15 acres of open field and scrub near a swampy area at East Claridon in 1937, reported by Isabelle Hellwig.

Nesting—Nest well concealed in bushes or small trees from 3 to 6 feet from the ground, built of rather coarse twigs, leaves and grasses, lined with fine rootlets or strips of grapevine bark. Two broods, sometimes three. Eggs 3, 4 or more. Nests with eggs reported from May 18 to August 2. Young in nest reported from June 5 to August 12.

EASTERN BROWN THRASHER — Toxostoma rufum rufum (Linnaeus)

STATUS—Common migrant; common summer resident; occasional in winter.

EARLIEST SPRING DATE—March 22, 1922. AVERAGE—April 12.

LATEST FALL DATE — October 13, 1934 and 1944. AVERAGE — October 2.

Winter records are December 11, 1942; December 29, 1947; January 5, 1944; January 2, 1943 (feeding on ivy berries all fall); January 1944 ("several times"), January 1948 ("seen repeatedly").

HABITAT AND DISTRIBUTION—Woodland border areas, thickets, open field and scrub, roadsides, dooryards, dry uplands. Generally distributed throughout the region.

NESTING—In thorn trees, bushes and thickets, not far from ground. Usually two broods. May 6, nest, 4 eggs; May 15-23, young; May 26, nest empty. May 26, nest, 2 young. May 24, nest building; May 27, 2 eggs; May 30-June 3, 3 eggs; June 15-24, young; June 30, nest empty. June 24, adults feeding 2 young out of nest. July 23, 1 young being fed away from nest.

Family TURDIDAE (Thrushes, Bluebirds)

EASTERN ROBIN—Turdus migratorius migratorius Linnaeus

STATUS—Abundant migrant; abundant summer resident.

AVERAGE SPRING DATE OF ARRIVAL—February 28. A flock of 80 robins "obviously migrating" has been reported as early as January 26 (1947).

AVERAGE FALL DATE OF DEPARTURE—October 22. On October 25, 1944, a "large southward movement" was noted.

The fact that robins so frequently spend the winter in the region makes it difficult, if not impossible, to assign first and last dates for migratory movements. Beginning in late August nightly "roosts" of robins become established, often in suburban residential areas. In such roosts from 1000 to 3000 birds have been estimated as congregating nightly for a period of weeks.

HABITAT AND DISTRIBUTION — The species is well distributed throughout the entire region. It apparently prefers association with human habitations, either in farming country, suburban residence communities, or even in built-up sections of cities. Some may always be found in more or less open woodlands or along forest edges. In autumn large flocks are often found in deep woods feeding on wild grapes or the fruits of tupelo trees. Several studies of breeding bird populations made within the region show the following densities of nesting robins: 15 acres, country estate at Gates Mills, 1937 to 1939 inclusive, an average of 13 pairs, reported by S. C. Kendeigh; 185 acres, Forest Hill Park, 1944, 44 pairs, reported by Kirtland Bird Club members; 39.1 acres, suburban residence areas in Cleveland Heights and Shaker Heights, 1941, 36 pairs, reported by M. W. Jacoby, R. W. Hill, A. B. Williams. It will be noted that the residence sections support about 1 robin pair per acre, while the more open park land averages about 1 pair per 4 acres. It is possible that 400,000 pairs of robins may breed annually in the area included in the Cleveland region.

NESTING—Frequently nests on or about buildings. Away from human habitations the nesting site is usually the crotch of a tree or a horizontal limb, varying from 3 to 35 feet from the ground, and even rarely, on the ground. From many records it appears that nest construction may begin as early as March 29. A nest with 3 young apparently several days old was reported April 13. Nesting activities are usually well under way by mid-April. Eggs, 3 to 5, usually 4. Incubation period 12 to 14 days. Two or three broods in a season. Nest with eggs reported as late as August 1.

NOTE—An albinistic strain seems to have become established among the robins in the eastern part of our region. Reports of either complete or partial albino robins are, in recent years, becoming more common.

BLACK-BACKED ROBIN—Turdus migratorius nigrideus
  Aldrich and Nutt

STATUS—Rare, probably occasional migrant.

In the collection of the CMNH are 2 specimens of this northeastern form which breeds in Newfoundland, Labrador and northern Quebec. Both were collected in Geauga County, a male March 22, a female April 18 (1930) (Aldrich and Nutt 1939:32).

WOOD THRUSH—Hylocichla mustelina (Gmelin)

STATUS—Common migrant; locally abundant summer resident.

EARLIEST SPRING DATE — April 6, 1941 and 1945. AVERAGE — April 19.

LATEST FALL DATE—October 20, 1946. AVERAGE—October 6.

HABITAT AND DISTRIBUTION—Frequents wooded areas, but like the robin is often found in wooded residential sections of the city. Generally distributed over the region. Its abundance as a breeding species in certain locations may be inferred from the fact that in a 65-acre tract of beech-maple-hemlock woodland over a period of 15 years, A. B. Williams reported an average of 14.3 pairs nesting annually. The maximum was 25 pairs in 1933, the minimum 6 pairs in 1937 and 1943 (Williams 1947:206).

NESTING—Nest usually in the crotch of a sapling 3 to 15 feet from the ground, or even as high as 40 feet in mature beech-maple forest. The bird seems to have a preference for small sugar maple trees as nesting sites. From many records the following are typical: May 11, nest nearing completion in small sugar maple; May 18, bird apparently incubating. May 25, nest, 4 eggs. May 29, nest in small beech 7 feet up, bird incubating 4 eggs. August 28, second brood leaving nest. June 30-July 4, female building nest; July 6-8, 3 eggs laid; July 20, 21, young visible in nest; August 1, 1 young left nest; August 2, second young left nest.

EASTERN HERMIT THRUSH—Hylocichla guttata faxoni
Bangs and Penard

STATUS—Common migrant; occasional in winter.

EARLIEST SPRING DATE — March 14, 1931. AVERAGE—March 25. LATEST—May 29, 1947.

EARLIEST FALL DATE—September 13, 1943. AVERAGE—September 24. LATEST—November 7, 1937.

Most numerous in April and October.

There appear to be two spring migration "waves". Of 165 records from March 14 to May 23, only 9 reports of this species occur from April 15 to May 1. The first wave seems to begin during the last few days of March and extends to the 15th of

April, while the second begins about May 1, gradually tapering off until the last recorded date, May 29.

Late records for this bird are: December 10, 1944; December 21, 1946; January 3 and 13, 1938; and one, probably the same bird, recorded 6 times December 21, 1947 to February 19, 1948. B. P. Bole, Jr. says, "One wintered, seen almost daily from January 15 to March 20, 1947, at 1712 Sheridan Road, South Euclid."

HABITAT AND DISTRIBUTION—Less shy than when in its normal breeding grounds, it migrates generally through this area but has a preference for deep woods, wooded swamps and stream valleys. Reports of the species in this region are from such places as the Metropolitan Parks, Doan Brook, Wade Park, Lakeview Cemetery, Mentor Headlands, and Little Mountain.

NESTING—Read (1853a:399) presumes that this is a nesting species here. Ingersoll (1883:304) lists it as "not a common summer resident; breeds." While it is possible that under more primitive conditions the hermit thrush may have nested here occasionally, there is no recent record of its having done so.

EASTERN OLIVE-BACKED THRUSH — Hylocichla ustulata swainsoni (Tschudi)

STATUS—Common migrant.

EARLIEST SPRING DATE—April 6, 1929. AVERAGE—April 27. LATEST —June 7, 1941.

EARLIEST FALL DATE—August 22, 1941. AVERAGE—September 9. LATEST—October 29, 1941.

Most common in May and September. Records indicate two spring waves, late April and early May. One bird reported December 11, 1918, by Doolittle (1919d:28).

HABITAT AND DISTRIBUTION—Usually this bird is seen on or near the ground in wooded areas, and when approached usually flies low from tree to tree, keeping well in advance, perching quietly on a branch until forced to move. It occurs all over the Cleveland area, and may be seen in such places as the Metropolitan Parks, cemeteries, wooded residential areas, and has been reported in downtown Cleveland.

WESTERN OLIVE-BACKED THRUSH — Hylocichla ustulata almae Oberholser

STATUS—Rare spring migrant.

In the collections of the CMNH are 6 specimens of this western form of the olive-backed thrush as follows: May 3, 1938, Richmond; May 9, 1930, Geauga Lake; May 12, 1935, Shaker Heights; May 17, 1923, Olmsted; May 25, 1931, North Olmsted; May 27, 1933, Cleveland.

GRAY-CHEEKED THRUSH—Hylocichla minima minima (Lafresnaye)

STATUS—Common to uncommon migrant.

EARLIEST SPRING DATE—April 12, 1938. AVERAGE—May 6. LATEST —June 2, 1947.

EARLIEST FALL DATE—August 24, 1941. LATEST—October 23, 1933.

Most numerous in May and September.

HABITAT AND DISTRIBUTION—Usually observed on or near the ground in woods and brushy situations. Well distributed over area from Rocky River Valley to Little Mountain.

VEERY—Hylocichla fuscescens fuscescens (Stephens)

STATUS—Common migrant; uncommon summer resident.

EARLIEST SPRING DATE—March 31, 1929. AVERAGE—April 23.

LATEST FALL DATE—October 6 (no year given—Bent 1949:230). AVERAGE—September 22.

HABITAT AND DISTRIBUTION—While generally distributed during migration, the favorite haunts of this bird are moist places such as bogs, stream bottoms, lakes, and swampy forests. In this region the Metropolitan Parks, Shaker Lakes, and wooded suburban sections are the most likely locations where it may be observed on migration. Read (1853a:399) declared this bird to be abundant here and to be found in damp, thick forests. Since that time the clearing of the land and drainage of swamps has cut down the number of suitable nesting areas.

NESTING—Nest on or near the ground, usually supported by the base of some plant or bush. May 31, nest, 3 eggs. May 14, nests

114

of 2 pairs. May 28, nest, 3 eggs; May 29, 4 eggs; all hatched in 12 days. May 30, nest, 4 eggs. May 13, adult bird building nest; May 16, nest completed; May 18, 3 eggs; June 3, 3 young; June 15, young left nest. J. W. Aldrich reported 2 pairs apparently nest building at Aurora Pond in June 1932.

WILLOW THRUSH—Hylocichla fuscescens salicicola Ridgway

STATUS—Rare and accidental migrant.

This western form of the veery is represented in our region by one male specimen found dead at the Terminal Tower in downtown Cleveland September 17, 1931, apparently having been killed by striking against the building during migration (Aldrich 1936a:98). Note by H. C. Oberholser indicates it is "intermediate" in character.

EASTERN BLUEBIRD—Sialia sialis sialis (Linnaeus)

STATUS—Common migrant; common summer resident.

EARLIEST SPRING DATE—February 13, 1938. AVERAGE—March 2. PEAK OF NUMBERS—About March 15.

LATEST FALL DATE—November 21, 1946. AVERAGE—October 28. PEAK OF NUMBERS—Last week in October.

Nine December and January records.

HABITAT AND DISTRIBUTION—Seen along roadsides, in orchards and open woods. Competition with the English sparrow and starling for nesting sites may have operated to decrease the abundance of this bird in recent times. It is certainly not as numerous now as it was before the advent of the starling. Well distributed over the region in open country environment.

NESTING—In old woodpecker holes, cavities in trees and fence posts, or in nesting boxes put up for its use. Usually 2 broods annually. March 13, mated and trying to dispossess English sparrow of bird box. April 24-26, old nest hole in fence post repaired or new nest built; April 29, first egg; April 30, second egg; May 1, third egg; May 2, fourth egg; May 3, fifth egg; May 18, young hatched, incubation period 12 days. June 20, nest with 4 young about half fledged. July 4, 4 eggs in nest box in wild black cherry on lawn; July 15, eggs still unhatched; July 16, female feeding young; August 2, two young left nest; August 3, two young left nest.

Family SYLVIIDAE (Warblers, Gnatcatchers and Kinglets)

BLUE-GRAY GNATCATCHER—Polioptila caerulea caerulea (Linnaeus)

STATUS—Not uncommon migrant; not uncommon summer resident.

EARLIEST SPRING DATE — April 9, 1919 and 1945. AVERAGE — April 25.

LATEST FALL DATE—October 10, 1937.

Very few September and October records.

HABITAT AND DISTRIBUTION—During migration generally distributed throughout the region, but preferring wooded sections, and observed in the Metropolitan Parks, Wade Park, Shaker Lakes, and outlying wooded areas. During breeding season seems to prefer lowland woods, usually in outlying country. It is one of the common nesting species about Hinckley Lake. After the breeding season they become quiet and retiring, few being seen in the late summer and early autumn months.

NESTING—Nest saddled on a horizontal branch or in a crotch of a tree, 10-60 feet from the ground. May 7, birds beginning nest construction in a small black walnut 30 feet up. May 11, old birds feeding young at nest. May 27, bird building nest. May 15, pair beginning nest building in willow swamp near river. May 21, bird building nest 10-12 feet from ground in apple tree near wading pool in Mastick picnic ground (Rocky River Metropolitan Park). May 24, nest with 3 eggs. May 25, birds gathering material and making nest high in oak tree. June 1, nest under construction. June 28, adults feeding young. June 30, female on nest; July 1, 2 eggs, 1 young; July 8, 1 young being fed by adults.

EASTERN GOLDEN-CROWNED KINGLET—Regulus satrapa satrapa Lichtenstein

STATUS—Common migrant; common winter visitor.

Because of the fact that this species is often present in numbers throughout the winter, it is difficult to determine when actual spring migration starts. Our records seem to indicate that this may be about March 10. A peak of numbers occurs about April 20.

EARLIEST FALL DATE—August 21, 1949.

LATEST SPRING DATE—May 22, 1947.

Most common in April and October.

HABITAT AND DISTRIBUTION — Frequents woodlands, brushy thickets, and coniferous trees. Generally distributed over the region during migration, and while it does occasionally visit residential sections, it is most often seen in the various parks, drives, and the woodlands of the surrounding country.

EASTERN RUBY-CROWNED KINGLET—Regulus calendula calendula (Linnaeus)

STATUS—Common migrant; rare winter visitor.

EARLIEST SPRING DATE — March 30, 1930. AVERAGE — April 12. LATEST—June 7, 1947.

EARLIEST FALL DATE—August 28, 1933. AVERAGE—September 26. LATEST—November 30, 1946.

There are a few scattering records for December, January and February, and two records of a bird wintering in the same locality. Heaviest migration periods are the second week in May and late October.

HABITAT AND DISTRIBUTION — Frequents woodlands, brushy thickets, and coniferous trees. Generally distributed over the region during migration, and observed in the Metropolitan Parks, various cemeteries, Wade Park, Shaker Lakes, Little Mountain, and outlying woodlands.

Family MOTACILLIDAE (Wagtails and Pipits)

AMERICAN PIPIT—Anthus spinoletta rubescens (Tunstall)

STATUS—Uncommon migrant; rare winter visitor.

EARLIEST SPRING DATE—March 8, 1942. LATEST—May 28, 1937.

EARLIEST FALL DATE — September 4, 1948. LATEST — December 20, 1938.

There are 3 January records. Most frequently observed during fall migration, being most numerous in November.

117

HABITAT AND DISTRIBUTION—Frequents cultivated and short grass fields, beaches, and mud flats. Usually travels in small or large flocks. Observed at such scattered places as White City, Fairport, Chesterland, Columbia, Shaker Lakes, Akron Lakes.

Family BOMBYCILLIDAE (Waxwings)

BOHEMIAN WAXWING—Bombycilla garrulus pallidiceps Reichenow

STATUS—Rare and irregular visitor.

Apparently this species was more frequently seen here formerly than is now the case. Kirtland (Wheaton 1882:217) writes: "A flock of Bohemian wax-chatterers *(Bombycilla garrula)*, consisting of fifty or sixty individuals, was frequently seen in a marsh at the old mouth of the Cuyahoga river, near the city of Cleveland during the month of March of the present year (1839?)." Again, Kirtland, in a letter dated July 17, 1845, mentions the Bohemian waxwing as among other species flying about his garden on that date, "thirty or forty specimens of which had been taken." (Wheaton 1882:295).

Read (1853a:343) says: "It visits us almost every winter and is frequently seen in various parts of the Reserve." Kirtland (1860) reports "a few" taken at Rockport (now Lakewood) in the winter of 1859-60, and adds (1874a:170) "sometimes in large flocks."

More recent records are February 23, 1909, at Chardon (Cook 1909). January 27, 1920, at Painesville, 75 seen; February 20, 1920, 6 seen; May 11, 1920, 1 seen (Doolittle 1920b). December 27, 1926, Mentor Marsh, 10 seen by A. B. Williams.

A flight of this species in the spring of 1944 seems to be indicated by the following reports: March 8, a flock of about 30 near the lake shore in Rocky River (Bohme, Corry). March 8-9, two at feeding station, Lyndhurst (Page). March 19, a pair, soon joined by 9 or 10 others, at feeding station in Lakewood (Sawyer). April 4, a flock of 9 seen twice in Lakewood (Olson).

HABITAT AND DISTRIBUTION—The place where this erratic and rare visitor to our region may appear is unpredictable. Wherever berries, such as are attractive to the cedar waxwing, are available in winter, the larger Bohemian waxwing may be looked for. At

118

any time of year all cedar waxwing flocks should be carefully scanned for the possibility of finding the larger species among them. The Bohemians also patronize feeding stations.

CEDAR WAXWING—Bombycilla cedrorum Vieillot

STATUS—Common migrant; common permanent resident.

HABITAT AND DISTRIBUTION—Overgrown fields, edges of ponds, roadsides and farmlands in the neighborhood of buildings, are favorite haunts of this species. In the autumn and winter they are attracted by berry-bearing shrubs, and particularly by fruits of the mountain ash. In old orchards they feast on frozen apples. Well distributed throughout the region, especially common in February and March. During winter frequently seen in flocks, numbering from 10 to 100 individuals. A flock estimated to contain 1000 birds was reported at Waite Hill November 4 and 5, 1939, by Mrs. Francis Sherwin.

NESTING — Characteristically one of the late nesting species. June 13, nest under construction; June 18, first egg laid; June 19, 20, 21, one egg laid each day (total 4) ; July 4, 2 eggs hatched; July 18, young left nest. July 29 to August 4, nest with eggs. July 13, nest in hawthorn hedge, 10 feet up, containing 3 nestlings, while a fourth young bird perched in nearby shrubbery. July 15, nest in maple sapling 7 feet up, 5 eggs. June 27, nest in thorn tree 5½ feet up, 4 eggs. July 7, nest in wild apple tree 5 feet up, 3 eggs. June 11, nest under construction 40 feet up in Lombardy poplar. July 3 and 6, nest, 3 eggs; July 17, 3 young a few days old; July 20, nest empty. July 13, nest 15 feet up, far out on limb of sycamore; July 20, old bird feeding small young in nest. August 21, nest in small maple on lawn, 2 eggs. September 16, nest with 4 young.

Family LANIIDAE (Shrikes)

NORTHERN SHRIKE—Lanius excubitor borealis Vieillot

STATUS—Rare winter visitor.

EARLIEST FALL DATE—November 4, 1941. AVERAGE (of 4 November dates)—November 18.

LATEST SPRING DATE—April 6, 1923. AVERAGE (of 5 February dates and 1 March date)—February 10.

119

HABITAT AND DISTRIBUTION—Usually this bird is seen perched on the top of some isolated small tree overlooking open fields or old orchards. All of the records of occurrence which we have (except 2) are from the area east and northeast of Cleveland. There is 1 record for East 82nd Street, Cleveland, and 1 from Willow (south of Cleveland). Most of the records are fairly close to the Lake Erie shore.

MIGRANT SHRIKE—Lanius ludovicianus migrans Palmer

STATUS—Uncommon migrant; uncommon summer resident.

EARLIEST SPRING DATE—March 13, 1938. AVERAGE—March 22.

LATEST FALL DATE—While we have many records of this species from March through July, beyond that time the bird seems to fade out of existence. Our only late records are August 6, 1942; August 6, 7, 1936; August 30, 1937; September 29, 1946; October 5, 1942; and October 11, 1943.

Apparently this species is decreasing in numbers in the region.

HABITAT AND DISTRIBUTION—Open fields, orchards and roadsides where overgrown thorn hedges, brush piles or thorn trees occur. Often seen perched on telephone or light wires or in bare branches of a dead tree. Sparingly distributed through farming sections of the region.

NESTING—The favorite nesting site of this species with us is in an old overgrown osage orange hedgerow, such as a few years ago was common along country roadsides east of Cleveland. March 30, nest construction beginning in thorn tree 10 feet up; April 22, bird incubating; May 6, 5 eggs. April 25, nest in osage hedge, 5 eggs. April 27, nest in thorn tree, 6 eggs probably incubated 3 to 4 days; May 14, young in nest possibly 3-4 days old. April 29, 7 eggs. May 5, nest in osage hedge, 1 egg. May 6, nest in pear tree about 8 feet up, 7 eggs; May 13, naked young in nest. May 17, nest in dead pear tree 8 feet up, 3 fully fledged young out of nest. May 26, old bird feeding young in nest. April 29, nest, 5 eggs; May 11, 1 egg hatched; May 12, 13, 3 eggs hatched; May 17, 3 fledglings; June 3, birds out of nest. June 10, 4 eggs; June 16, 4 naked young; June 27, young fully feathered; June 30, 4 young left nest.

Family STURNIDAE (Starlings)

STARLING—Sturnus vulgaris vulgaris Linnaeus

STATUS—Abundant permanent resident.

The starling, a native of Europe, was first successfully introduced into the United States in 1890, when 80 birds were released in Central Park, New York City. The first mention of the bird in the Cleveland region seems to be that of 20 starlings seen August 10, 1920, in the vicinity of Painesville, reported by Doolittle (1921:35). It is first mentioned in the Cleveland Bird Calendar of 1924, Bulletin No. 1, as follows: "Through December 1923 and January 1924 one fed at food box of Mrs. V. W. Terrell, 2041 Taylor Road, East Cleveland, and several birds appeared early in February." Since that time the starling has become one of the most common birds of the region.

E. C. Hoffman, writing in the Cleveland Bird Calendar of 1932, Bulletin No. 1, says: "Starlings first appeared on Cleveland Public Square October 13, 1930. Maximum numbers during winter of 1930-31 were reached on November 14, when 5250 roosted about the Square. During the next winter (1931-32) two new buildings were occupied (Marshall Building and Public Library). The majority roosted on the Post Office Building (Federal Building). On December 10, estimated 7700; January 20, 12,100; February 27, 19,900; March 18, 6480; March 19, 3025. The rapid reduction from 20,000 to 6480 began with the onset of the cold period March 6. Starlings banded in Cleveland and Lakewood have been reported from Mississippi and Quebec, indicating a possible migration route following the Mississippi and St. Lawrence River Systems."

In the Cleveland Bird Calendar of 1931, Bulletin No. 1, "flock after flock" were reported moving eastward along the Lake Erie shore, January 22.

On December 10, 1932 (Cleveland Bird Calendar, Bulletin No. 4, 1932) it was estimated that 15,000 starlings were roosting nightly on buildings about the Cleveland Public Square.

HABITAT AND DISTRIBUTION—In farming country, suburban residence areas, city buildings, in fact everywhere except in forested areas, this species is commonly found. In fall and winter, starlings often congregate in enormous flocks, roosting together during the night and dispersing over the surrounding country by day to gather food.

NESTING—In holes in trees, crevices in buildings, and in nesting boxes usually put up to attract other birds. April 18, nest, 7 eggs. May 3, nest, 5 eggs. May 6, nest with eggs. May 19, young in nesting hole being fed by old birds.

Family VIREONIDAE (Vireos)

NORTHERN WHITE-EYED VIREO—Vireo griseus noveboracensis (Gmelin)

STATUS—Rare and accidental migrant.

There are about 30 records for this bird in the region—mostly May dates.

EARLIEST SPRING DATE—April 29, 1948. AVERAGE—May 18.

LATEST FALL DATE—September 22, 1940.

HABITAT AND DISTRIBUTION—During migration reported from Shaker Lakes, Wade Park, Gordon Park, Novelty, Berea, North Olmsted, Virginia Kendall State Park, Rocky River, the Chagrin Valley, and from residential sections.

NESTING—Ingersoll (1883:304) lists this species as "not common summer resident; breeds", but we have no positive breeding record.

YELLOW-THROATED VIREO—Vireo flavifrons Vieillot

STATUS—Common migrant; common summer resident.

EARLIEST SPRING DATE—April 13, 1947. AVERAGE—May 7.

LATEST FALL DATE—October 17, 1938. AVERAGE—September 22.

HABITAT AND DISTRIBUTION — These birds are usually seen or heard in high forest trees in all forest types. Distribution quite general over the area. In a 15-year study at North Chagrin, A. B. Williams found an average of 2.2 pairs nesting in 65 acres of beech-maple forest, fluctuating from 7 pairs to 1. H. E. Wallin found 7 pairs nesting in a 50-acre tract of oak-hickory forest at Brecksville in 1941; 3 pairs in 1947. Moulthrop and Williams found 4 pairs in 31 acres of woodland at the Holden Arboretum in 1939; Walters and Williams, 3 pairs in 1941.

NESTING—May 15, Aurora Pond, nest in large white oak 50 feet up; May 22, adults feeding young in nest. May 19, North Akron, nest construction started. May 19, Brecksville, nest construction begun in a red oak about 60 feet up. June 11, Aurora, bird carrying food to nest.

BLUE-HEADED VIREO—Vireo solitarius solitarius (Wilson)

STATUS—Common migrant; rare summer resident.

EARLIEST SPRING DATE—April 4, 1946. AVERAGE—May 1. PEAK OF NUMBERS—May 16.

LATEST FALL DATE—November 3, 1946. AVERAGE—September 28.

HABITAT AND DISTRIBUTION—During migration the blue-headed vireo has been reported from many of the Metropolitan Parks, as well as from the Holden Arboretum, Solon Bog and Shaker Lakes.

NESTING—B. P. Bole, Jr. reports that 2 pairs nested on Little Mountain in an upland pine-hemlock-red maple forest in 1937, and another pair was seen regularly here during June and July of that year. He also reports observing 3 males, all singing, in widely scattered territories, in Stebbin's Gulch on June 20, 1947. On June 20, 1938, he located a nest in a white pine about 100 feet up, suspended between 2 living twigs in thick spray of branchlets; bird observed carrying caterpillars to nest.

RED-EYED VIREO—Vireo olivaceus (Linnaeus)

STATUS—Common migrant; locally abundant summer resident.

EARLIEST SPRING DATE—April 8, 1945. AVERAGE—May 5.

LATEST FALL DATE—November 25, 1931. AVERAGE—October 1.

HABITAT AND DISTRIBUTION—Frequents all forest types as well as second growth or open woodlands and even isolated trees. Often found in suburban residence areas. Generally distributed over the region wherever trees are found. Included in practically all breeding bird population studies within the region where nesting sites in trees are available.

In a 65-acre tract of beech-maple-hemlock forest at North Chagrin, over a 15-year period, this bird always appeared as the most abundant nesting species, the average being 25.4 pairs nesting annually. The highest number was 36 pairs in 1933, the lowest 18 pairs in 1940 (Williams 1947:206). In a 50-acre tract of oak-hickory forest at Brecksville, Harold E. Wallin found 8 pairs nesting in 1947.

NESTING—The location of the nest varies considerably from a few feet above the ground to well up in tall trees. The nest is suspended from a horizontal fork of small twigs, usually in a deciduous tree. The bird has, however, been found at North Chagrin nesting in hemlock. The earliest date for completed nest or nest with eggs is May 30, the latest August 16, the average June 28. The greatest number of eggs found in any one nest is 3.

PHILADELPHIA VIREO—Vireo philadelphicus (Cassin)

STATUS—Not uncommon migrant.

EARLIEST SPRING DATE — April 30, 1938. AVERAGE — May 15. LATEST—June 2, 1940.

EARLIEST FALL DATE—August 26, 1945. AVERAGE—September 30. LATEST—October 26, 1946.

HABITAT AND DISTRIBUTION — Generally distributed throughout the region during spring and fall migrations. Frequently seen at Shaker Lakes, Holden Arboretum, Metropolitan Parks.

EASTERN WARBLING VIREO—Vireo gilvus gilvus (Vieillot)

STATUS—Common migrant; not uncommon summer resident.

EARLIEST SPRING DATE—April 25, 1948. AVERAGE—May 2.

LATEST FALL DATE—October 12, 1935. AVERAGE—September 20.

HABITAT AND DISTRIBUTION—Found in a variety of habitats, parks, suburban residential districts, and along country roadsides.

NESTING—The favorite nesting site of this bird is medium to large trees bordering country roads, or in dooryards. Also in apple orchards. The fact that this bird habitually sings on its nest makes its location rather easy to find. April 25, nest under construction 35 feet up in sycamore; May 24, bird on new nest about 25 feet from the first one, 10 feet up in elm. June 6, 4 eggs, nest 25 feet up in apple tree in large orchard. June 6, 3 eggs, nest 20 feet up in apple tree in large orchard; nested regularly in this orchard several years. June 12, bird incubating eggs in nest 17 feet up in fork of elm; June 23-28, 30, July 3, adult feeding young in nest; July 5, adults feeding 3 young in tree near one containing nest.

Family PARULIDAE (Wood Warblers)

BLACK AND WHITE WARBLER—Mniotilta varia (Linnaeus)

STATUS—Common migrant; possible rare summer resident.

EARLIEST SPRING DATE—April 8, 1945. AVERAGE—April 30. PEAK OF NUMBERS—First week in May. LATEST—June 12, 1949.

EARLIEST FALL DATE—July 8, 1945. AVERAGE—August 11. LATEST —November 28, 1948.

HABITAT AND DISTRIBUTION—Although this is a woodland bird, and may often be seen on the bark of trees behaving like a creeper, it is not restricted to woodlands during migration. Well distributed over the region.

NESTING—Ingersoll (1883:304) says "a few remain and breed." E. E. Hammett, Jr. (1891) reported a nest with 5 young recently hatched found April 28. The nest was "in a crack of the trunk of a large tree . . . composed of fibers and dried leaves, lined with hair and soft cotton like down." J. E. Lieftinck saw a bird of this species at Hinckley June 28, 1936, "behaving like a resident bird."

PROTHONOTARY WARBLER—Protonotaria citrea (Boddaert)

STATUS—Uncommon migrant; uncommon summer resident.

EARLIEST SPRING DATE—May 4, 1913. AVERAGE—May 17.

LATEST FALL DATE—August 22, 1949.

HABITAT AND DISTRIBUTION—This is a bird of swampy pond or stream margins or wooded swamps, where dead stubs of trees containing old woodpecker holes or hollows offer acceptable nesting sites. On migration it has been recorded from Shaker Lakes, Lakeview Cemetery and Rocky River Valley, as well as in its more characteristic haunts, the eastern end of Mentor Marsh, the northern end of Aurora Pond, the meanders of the Cuyahoga River near Welshfield, and the swampy margins of Bass Lake.

NESTING—The first evidence of the nesting of this species within our region was the report that on June 9, 1912, at Bass Lake, an adult was observed carrying food as though to a nest. The species had been previously observed at Bass Lake in 1907, and again June 12, 1910 (Cook 1915a).

The first discovery of a nest of these warblers in the region was made by John W. Aldrich June 13, 1939, at Aurora Pond, when a pair of birds were seen and the nest, containing 3 young and an egg just hatching, located in a hollow stub.

The presence of breeding birds at Aurora Pond was further confirmed when 2 adults feeding 2 well-fledged young were observed there June 22, 1946, by Merit B. Skaggs and F. A. Simpson. On June 21, 1947, Jerry Piskac located a nest, apparently with young, in a dead birch stub in a flooded forest area at the south end of Aurora Pond; June 22, the above nest was visited by boat by Mr. and Mrs. Klein and Mr. and Mrs. Skaggs, who found 3 good-sized birds therein with 1 infertile egg. A second nest in a birch stub was found to be too high to investigate. A third nest was found to contain 2 young cowbirds ready to leave the nest and 3 young warblers. Skaggs also found a nest near Welshfield (Cuyahoga River) June 29, 1947. The nest was in a hollow stump at the river edge and contained 4 young and 1 infertile egg. Young still in nest, but nearly ready to leave, July 3 (Skaggs 1948).

On May 29, 1948, a nest was found at Aurora Pond by Adela Gaede in a hole in a dead tree 50 feet from shore, the hole 5 feet from the water. The male brought food to the female, who appeared to feed young. On May 31, 1948, at Aurora Pond, C. T. Downer observed a female going in and out of a hole 8 feet up in a black cherry stump standing in the water, the male singing nearby.

On June 11, 1948, at Aurora Pond, Carl Hamann discovered a nest in the top of a yellow birch stub, 8 feet above the water. Adults were carrying food to the hole, apparently feeding young.

On August 8, 1948, at Black Brook, George King observed a male carrying food to 3 fledglings able to fly; and on August 15 at the same place, a female feeding 4 young, all lined up in the same way.

WORM-EATING WARBLER—Helmitheros vermivorus (Gmelin)

STATUS—Rare and accidental migrant.

EARLIEST SPRING DATE—April 28, 1938. LATEST—May 29, 1913.

All of our records of the occurrence of this more southern bird in our region are for individuals observed during the month of May. The dates cover 13 different years, from 1913 to 1945. Reported by 10 different observers.

HABITAT AND DISTRIBUTION—Reported from Willoughby, Cuyahoga Falls, Wade Park, Shaker Lakes, Lakeview Cemetery, Cuyahoga Valley, Garfield Park, City of Cleveland, Akron Lakes, Hinckley Lake. Also reported from Wellington May 19, 1940.

GOLDEN-WINGED WARBLER—Vermivora chrysoptera (Linnaeus)

STATUS—Uncommon migrant; possible rare summer resident.

EARLIEST SPRING DATE—May 6, 1943 and 1947. AVERAGE—May 14.

LATEST FALL DATE—September 5, 1943.

HABITAT AND DISTRIBUTION—We have very little information as to the status of this species in our region. All records but one are early spring dates of occurrence. One of these, the latest date seen, is in the Rocky River Valley. The other 21 are east of Cleveland. Single birds observed May 8, 9, 16, 18, 19, 22, 1948; and 2 birds on May 11, 1948. The occurrence here of hybrids between this species and the blue-winged warbler (Brewster's warbler and Lawrence's warbler) suggests the possibility of the golden-wing being a possible occasional summer resident.

BLUE-WINGED WARBLER—Vermivora pinus (Linnaeus)

STATUS—Common migrant; not uncommon summer resident.

EARLIEST SPRING DATE—April 17, 1949. AVERAGE—May 3.

LATEST FALL DATE—November 14, 1948. AVERAGE—September 20.

HABITAT AND DISTRIBUTION—The favorite haunt of this species is the swampy margins of woods and moist open woodland paths where there is an abundance of herbaceous ground cover. It is well distributed east and south in the region, but we lack any record west of the Rocky River Valley.

NESTING—Nest built a few inches above the ground, usually in the midst of a clump of grass, weeds, or other vegetation (in one instance, a clump of violets). May 11, beginning nest construction. May 20, nest, 3 eggs. May 22, nest, 3 eggs. May 24, nest under construction 3 inches off the ground; June 2, 5 fresh eggs. May 30, nest, 4 eggs. June 17, young left nest.

BREWSTER'S WARBLER—Vermivora leucobronchialis (Brewster)

STATUS—Rare migrant; possible rare summer resident.

Five sight records for this hybrid between the blue-winged and golden-winged warblers have been reported for the region. May 19, 1940, Rocky River Valley (McQuown); May 19, 1945, Lakewood (Olson); June 20, 1928, Auburn (Watterson); August 29, 1939, Brecksville (O'Reilly); August 29, 1944, Shaker Lakes (Newman). We include the bird in our list as a possible summer resident because the blue-winged warbler is a not uncommon summer resident of the region, and although uncommon, the golden-winged warbler's range appears to overlap with the blue-winged's here. Under these circumstances hybridization is said to occur commonly, although our present records are insufficient to establish this as having occurred here.

LAWRENCE'S WARBLER—Vermivora lawrencei (Herrick)

STATUS—Rare migrant; possible rare summer resident.

We have two sight records only. May 13, 1945, made at Silver Lake by Charles P. Mountz; and August 23, 1939, at Brecksville by Ralph O'Reilly. This is the "recessive" hybrid between blue-winged warbler and golden-winged warbler, and is included in our list as a possible summer resident for the same reason that the Brewster's warbler is so included.

TENNESSEE WARBLER—Vermivora peregrina (Wilson)

STATUS—Common migrant.

EARLIEST SPRING DATE—May 1, 1927. AVERAGE—May 9. LATEST —May 30, 1931, 1941, 1946.

128

EARLIEST FALL DATE—August 20, 1940 and 1941. AVERAGE—September 2. LATEST—October 20, 1946.

HABITAT AND DISTRIBUTION—This is a bird of the trees, often being seen high up in large trees. Well distributed over the region during migration, including suburban residence areas.

ORANGE-CROWNED WARBLER—Vermivora celata celata (Say)

STATUS—Rare migrant.

EARLIEST SPRING DATE—April 20, 1941. AVERAGE—May 8. LATEST —May 30, 1938.

EARLIEST FALL DATE—August 23, 1941. LATEST—October 13, 1945.

HABITAT AND DISTRIBUTION—On migration is usually seen in trees or shrubbery in suburban residence communities or along woods edges or in more open woodlands. Nearly all of our records are for areas east of the Cuyahoga Valley. One record for Rocky River Valley.

NASHVILLE WARBLER—Vermivora ruficapilla ruficapilla (Wilson)

STATUS—Common migrant.

EARLIEST SPRING DATE—April 8, 1945. AVERAGE—May 2. LATEST —June 1, 1947.

EARLIEST FALL DATE — August 3, 1941. AVERAGE — August 21. LATEST—October 24, 1946.

HABITAT AND DISTRIBUTION—On migration may be looked for in parks or open woodlands. Often it appears along the bushy margins of ponds or swampy areas. Well distributed over the region.

NORTHERN PARULA WARBLER—Parula americana pusilla (Wilson)

STATUS—Uncommon migrant.

EARLIEST SPRING DATE—May 3, 1942. AVERAGE—May 6. LATEST— June 27, 1942.

EARLIEST FALL DATE — August 16, 1943. AVERAGE—August 28. LATEST—October 18, 1948.

HABITAT AND DISTRIBUTION — On migration may be found almost anywhere where there are bushes and trees, except in deep woodlands. Usually noted rather high up in trees.

EASTERN YELLOW WARBLER—Dendroica petechia aestiva (Gmelin)

STATUS—Common migrant; common summer resident.

EARLIEST SPRING DATE—April 16, 1937 and 1939. AVERAGE—May 1.

LATEST FALL DATE—October 19, 1932. AVERAGE—September 15.

HABITAT AND DISTRIBUTION—Scrubby fields, the edges of bogs and ponds, farmlands, and suburban residence areas are all attractive localities for this warbler. It is well distributed throughout the region. In a 5-year study (1943-1947) of a 15.3-acre tract of pond and border, Vera Carrothers found an average of 6.2 pairs nesting annually. Numbers of pairs varied from 4 in 1946 to 8 in 1943 and 1944.

NESTING—While this bird seems to have a preference for the vicinity of water, where it nests in bushes and small willows from 3 to 8 feet up, it also nests in brambles or small trees in overgrown scrubby pastures, or even in the smaller shade trees along suburban, city or town streets, sometimes as high up as 40 feet. From a study of numerous nesting records it appears that nest construction is usually begun May 10-15, eggs are 3 to 5, young leave nest about third week in June.

MAGNOLIA WARBLER—Dendroica magnolia (Wilson)

STATUS—Common migrant; possible rare summer resident.

EARLIEST SPRING DATE—April 20, 1948. AVERAGE—May 6. LATEST —June 20, 1947.

EARLIEST FALL DATE — July 28, 1946. AVERAGE — September 2. LATEST—November 2, 1937.

HABITAT AND DISTRIBUTION—On migration may be found almost anywhere where there are trees. Well distributed throughout the region.

NESTING—Ingersoll (1883:304) lists this species as an abundant spring and fall migrant and says, "a few remain and breed." B.

P. Bole, Jr. reports observing a male magnolia warbler in Stebbin's Gulch June 20, 1947, singing, catching flies, and carrying them off as if to a nest. From May 30 to July 3, 1949, at least 3 singing males were present in Stebbin's Gulch, and on one occasion one was seen to be carrying food as if to young birds. Observers were Carrothers, Hill, Newman and Ramisch.

CAPE MAY WARBLER—Dendroica tigrina (Gmelin)

STATUS—Common migrant.

EARLIEST SPRING DATE—April 27, 1938. AVERAGE—May 6. LATEST —May 27, 1947.

EARLIEST FALL DATE—August 20, 1941. AVERAGE—August 29. LATEST—December 5, 1943.

HABITAT AND DISTRIBUTION—On migration may be found almost anywhere where there are trees and shrubbery. Well distributed throughout the region.

BLACK-THROATED BLUE WARBLER—Dendroica caerulescens caerulescens (Gmelin)

STATUS—Not uncommon migrant.

EARLIEST SPRING DATE—April 25, 1948. AVERAGE—May 7. LATEST —May 30, 1931, 1945 and 1948.

On May 4, 1936, a migrating flock of 200 was reported on Little Mountain.

EARLIEST FALL DATE—August 21, 1941. AVERAGE—September 6. LATEST—October 28, 1945.

HABITAT AND DISTRIBUTION—On migration may be found in semi-open country, as well as in woodlands. Records from Shaker Lakes, Little Mountain, Gordon Park, Fairport, North Chagrin, Aurora Pond, Hinckley Lake, Holden Arboretum and Rocky River indicate a wide distribution throughout the region.

MYRTLE WARBLER—Dendroica coronata coronata (Linnaeus)

STATUS—Common migrant; occasional in winter.

EARLIEST SPRING DATE—March 7, 1948. AVERAGE—April 17. LATEST —May 30, 1947.

EARLIEST FALL DATE—August 6, 1942. AVERAGE—September 10. LATEST—November 29, 1947.

On April 27, 1942, an estimated 150 birds were present about Shaker Lake. On October 14, 1948, about 100 birds at Shaker Lake and many others reported from Shaker Heights and Lakewood indicated a heavy migratory movement on this date. Winter records are: December 6, 26, 27(11), 1947; December 8, 21, 1946; December 21, 1946; December 22, 1940; December 27, 1940 to January 7, 1941, one at feeding station in Parma; January 12, 1883, specimen collected at Rockport (now Lakewood) (Hall 1883:32).

HABITAT AND DISTRIBUTION—On migration found in woodlands as well as in more open situations, including bushes and shrubbery. Well distributed throughout the region.

ALASKA MYRTLE WARBLER—Dendroica coronata hooveri McGregor

STATUS—Rare and accidental visitor.

A specimen of this western race of the myrtle warbler in the collections of the CMNH was collected at Mentor Headlands April 14, 1931, by J. W. Aldrich. Identification was made by W. Earl Godfrey, corroborated by Dr. Harry C. Oberholser (Godfrey 1943c).

AUDUBON'S WARBLER—Dendroica auduboni auduboni (Townsend)

STATUS—Rare and accidental migrant.

This common warbler of the west has been reported three times in our region: April 30 and May 3, 1931, at Shaker Lake, by W. H. Watterson (1931); and October 5, 1941, at Richmond, by W. Earl Godfrey and Ruth Newcomer (Godfrey 1943a). Of this latter record Godfrey says, "Apparently an adult male in post-nuptial plumage. A beautifully marked (for autumn) specimen. Observed under excellent conditions making identification easy and complete."

BLACK-THROATED GRAY WARBLER—Dendroica nigrescens (J. K. Townsend)

STATUS—Rare and accidental visitor.

This western species has been reported in our region 8 times, always during the month of May. Dates are: May 12, 1920;

132

May 25, 1924; May 30, 1924; May 31, 1924; May 14, 1927; May 17, 1929; May 9, 1938; May 25, 1940. These are all for single birds except May 9, 1938, when 3 were reported by B. P. Bole, Jr., on Little Mountain. Observers were Prof. W. H. Hulme, Donald Hulme, B. P. Bole, Jr., and Margaret Sherwin.

HABITAT AND DISTRIBUTION—Localities from which birds have been reported are Wade Park (twice), Little Mountain (twice), Shaker Lake, Gates Mills, Rockefeller Park, Waite Hill.

BLACK-THROATED GREEN WARBLER—Dendroica virens virens (Gmelin)

STATUS—Common migrant; locally common summer resident.

EARLIEST SPRING DATE—April 8, 1945. AVERAGE—April 30.

LATEST FALL DATE — November 18, 1948. AVERAGE (of October dates)—October 11.

Heavy migrations reported in early May and early September. Locally abundant during breeding season.

HABITAT AND DISTRIBUTION—During migration may be found almost anywhere where there are trees, but during nesting period restricted to concentrations of coniferous trees. Such locations are largely found in the Chagrin River drainage system east of Cleveland, including Little Mountain, Holden Arboretum, North and South Chagrin Reservations, and contiguous territory.

On Little Mountain this warbler is the most abundant nesting species, as determined by breeding bird population studies conducted by B. P. Bole, Jr. in 1933, 1935, 1936, 1937, 1938. From 10 to 19 pairs were found nesting in the 75-acre tract under study. This location also attracts many migrating birds of this species, counts of as many as 50 individuals having been made there October 14, 1935, and May 4, 1936.

NESTING—In hemlock trees, usually so high up that observations of nesting activities are impossible or unsatisfactory. Young birds were noted at North Chagrin July 19, 1943.

CERULEAN WARBLER—Dendroica cerulea (Wilson)

STATUS—Not uncommon migrant; locally common summer resident.

EARLIEST SPRING DATE—April 25, 1948. AVERAGE—May 5.

LATEST FALL DATE—October 2, 1935. AVERAGE—September 17.

HABITAT AND DISTRIBUTION—Except on migration, prefers more open woodlands. Well distributed east, west and south throughout the region, nesting in pine-hemlock (Little Mountain), beech-maple (North Chagrin, South Chagrin), oak-hickory (Brecksville), second growth woodland (Hinckley), flood plain forest (Rocky River), oak-hickory (Westlake). In the Brecksville Reservation this warbler is next to the most abundant nesting species, as determined by the breeding bird population studies conducted by Harold E. Wallin in 1941, 1942, 1943, 1946 and 1947. From 8 to 17 pairs were found nesting in the 50-acre tract under study.

NESTING—Mentioned by Kirtland (1874a:170) as regularly breeding here prior to 1852. Nests in deciduous forests or open woodlands, usually in large trees, 30 to 100 feet up. Nest construction begun in two instances May 19, in another, May 21. Nest, 3 eggs, June 4. Female observed feeding well-developed young in nest June 16. June 18, nest, 2 young, 1 young out of nest.

BLACKBURNIAN WARBLER—Dendroica fusca (Müller)

STATUS—Common migrant; rare summer resident.

EARLIEST SPRING DATE—April 19, 1942. AVERAGE—May 5. LATEST —June 5, 1931.

EARLIEST FALL DATE—August 15, 1942. AVERAGE—September 5. LATEST—October 20, 1946.

HABITAT AND DISTRIBUTION—On migration may be looked for high up in trees, both in open situations and in deep woodlands. Well distributed over the region.

NESTING—In connection with a study of the breeding bird population of a 75-acre tract of pine-hemlock forest on Little Mountain, B. P. Bole, Jr. reported 1 nesting pair in 1933; 2 nesting pairs in 1934. Bole also reported seeing an adult female blackburnian warbler on Little Mountain July 18, 1938.

SYCAMORE WARBLER—Dendroica dominica albilora Ridgway

STATUS—Rare migrant.

Probably all of the records we have of the "yellow-throated warbler" or "yellow-throated wood warbler" or "yellow throated gray warbler" refer to this western race (*D. d. albilora*).

Kirtland says of the "yellow throated gray warbler", "during the last week in April of the present year (probably 1840), I killed three near the Cuyahoga river, three miles from Lake Erie." He also included this species as among those "annually rearing their young in this region." (Wheaton 1882:218,193). This is probably the basis for Read's statement that "a few reach as far north as Lake Erie and nest here." (Read 1853a:415). One was reported by Chubb (1880) April 19, 1880.

More recent records are: One seen at "Mayfield Road" May 15, 1913 (W. H. Hulme); one at Shaker Lake May 8, 1924, and another at Rockefeller Park May 9, 1924 (Eastman, Kimmel and Hulme).

The sycamore warbler has been reported near Painesville May 18, 1913, by Doolittle (1914); at Gordon Park May 24, 1936 (Bole); near the Holden Arboretum April 24, 1948 (Bole, Robert S. Smith). This last record was made under ideal conditions, making identification very complete and satisfactory.

CHESTNUT-SIDED WARBLER—Dendroica pensylvanica (Linnaeus)

STATUS—Common migrant; rare summer resident.

EARLIEST SPRING DATE—April 19, 1908. AVERAGE—May 5. LATEST —May 30, 1938.

EARLIEST FALL DATE—August 23, 1930. AVERAGE—September 7. LATEST—October 12, 1948.

There are several scattering summer records which may or may not represent migrating birds: June 2, 1947; June 3, 1945; June 13, 22, 1934; June 22, 1933; July 4, 1938.

HABITAT AND DISTRIBUTION — On migration may be seen almost anywhere in bushes or trees. It particularly frequents woods edges and thickets. Well distributed east and south in the region, but no records west of Rocky River.

NESTING—There are two nesting records for the region. One reported from Sharline, Geauga County, May 27, 1919, building nest; June 12, nest with 3 eggs in "clump of scrubby beech" 2 feet from ground (Miller 1930:56). One reported by Dr. C. T. Downer at Novelty, June 23, 1917, nest with 4 eggs in clump of weeds about 12 inches from ground, on flood plain of the Chagrin River; June 30, 3 young birds and 1 egg.

BAY-BREASTED WARBLER—Dendroica castanea (Wilson)

STATUS—Common migrant.

EARLIEST SPRING DATE—April 20, 1941. AVERAGE—May 8. LATEST —June 11, 1945.

EARLIEST FALL DATE — July 28, 1946. AVERAGE—September 4. LATEST—October 17, 1935, 1938, 1946.

HABITAT AND DISTRIBUTION—On migration found in woodlands and parks where it spends most of its time in the upper levels of the trees. Well distributed throughout the region.

BLACK-POLL WARBLER—Dendroica striata (Forster)

STATUS—Common migrant.

EARLIEST SPRING DATE—April 25, 1948. AVERAGE—May 11. LATEST —June 2, 1928, 1940.

EARLIEST FALL DATE—August 8, 1941. AVERAGE—September 1. LATEST—October 27, 1946.

HABITAT AND DISTRIBUTION—On migration may be looked for in trees in parks and woodlands. Well distributed throughout the region. On Little Mountain B. P. Bole, Jr. classes it as a "common to abundant migrant."

NORTHERN PINE WARBLER—Dendroica pinus pinus (Wilson)

STATUS—Uncommon migrant.

EARLIEST SPRING DATE — April 14, 1912. AVERAGE — April 27. LATEST—May 27, 1945, 1947.

EARLIEST FALL DATE — August 1, 1938. AVERAGE — August 26. LATEST—October 20, 1946.

There are two July records for the species here: a female seen July 16 and 21, 1919, near Painesville by Doolittle (1919e:128); and 2 males observed on Little Mountain July 4 to July 18, 1938, by B. P. Bole, Jr.

HABITAT AND DISTRIBUTION—Prefers coniferous woods, although on migration is found in open deciduous woodlands as well. Records are from Little Mountain, Shaker Lakes, Gates Mills, Gordon Park, Rocky River Valley, and Hinckley Lake.

KIRTLAND'S WARBLER—Dendroica kirtlandii (Baird)

STATUS—Rare migrant.

This bird is of special interest to the members of the Kirtland Society, since it bears the name of Dr. Kirtland, after whom the Society is named, and because the type specimen was collected near the Kirtland home, now within the limits of the City of Lakewood.

The first specimen of this warbler known to science, an adult male, was collected by Charles Pease on the grounds of Dr. Jared P. Kirtland in the Village of Rockport (now 14013 Detroit Avenue, Lakewood) May 13, 1851. It was presented to Dr. Kirtland, and by him sent to Prof. Spencer F. Baird of the United States National Museum in Washington for identification. Recognized by Baird as a new species, it was first described by him and named after Kirtland, "a gentleman to whom, more than anyone living, we are indebted for a knowledge of the natural history of the Mississippi Valley." (Baird 1852:218).

It was nine years before R. K. Winslow of Cleveland, who was an indefatigable collector of birds, secured a second specimen, a female shot by Mr. Darby of University Heights, near the "old river bed", Cleveland. The locality referred to is probably that now occupied by ore docks just west of the mouth of the Cuyahoga River. The year was 1860, and the month probably May (Kirkpatrick 1860).

Other early records, while rather confused as to detail, are definite as to dates. They are as follows: May 3, 1878, a male and a female taken at Rockport by A. Hall within 2 miles of the place where the type specimen was secured (Wheaton 1879a; Jones 1904b:112). May 4 and 12, 1880, a specimen collected on each date (male and female) by H. E. Chubb, near Cleveland (Chubb 1880; Langdon 1880:123).

Since these early records no specimens of the Kirtland's warbler have been taken in the Cleveland region.

We have a number of relatively recent sight records which, because of the rarity of the bird and the fact that the observations were made by individuals unaccompanied by others, might be open to some question. These are as follows: October 7, 1934(2), September 2, 1935(1), September 8, 1940(1), October 5, 1941(2), September 26, 1943(1), September 8, 1946(2), all reported by J. O. McQuown for an area in the Rocky River Valley approximately between Hilliard and Detroit Avenues. May 18, 1943(1), reported by Tom McHugh as seen in Lakewood. If these later records are accepted as valid they might well suggest a possible regular migration route through the Cleveland region for this rare warbler which nests in Michigan and winters in the Bahamas.

NORTHERN PRAIRIE WARBLER—Dendroica discolor discolor (Vieillot)

STATUS—Rare migrant.

EARLIEST SPRING DATE—April 12, 1943. AVERAGE—May 11. LATEST —May 30, 1924.

EARLIEST FALL DATE—July 26, 1925. LATEST—September 23, 1941.

HABITAT AND DISTRIBUTION—On migration is found in small trees and shrubbery, often on or near the ground. All our records come from areas east of Cleveland.

NESTING—The only evidence of possible nesting in our region is the statement attributed to Kirtland that this species "sometimes rears its young near the shores of Lake Erie" (Read 1853a:423). Wheaton (1882:193) quotes Kirtland as saying that certain warblers (including the prairie warbler) "annually rear their young in this vicinity." There are no recent records indicating nesting here, however.

WESTERN PALM WARBLER—Dendroica palmarum palmarum (Gmelin)

STATUS—Common migrant.

EARLIEST SPRING DATE—April 15, 1945. AVERAGE—May 1. LATEST —May 26, 1940.

EARLIEST FALL DATE—August 30, 1948. AVERAGE—September 16. LATEST—October 25, 1942.

There is an unusual record for July 28, 1946, and another for a bird at a feeding station at Olmsted Falls eating suet January 4, 1941.

HABITAT AND DISTRIBUTION—Usually seen in underbrush near or on the ground. On migration widely distributed over the region, many records coming from Shaker Lake, Gordon Park, Holden Arboretum and Rocky River.

EASTERN OVENBIRD—Seiurus aurocapillus aurocapillus (Linnaeus)

STATUS—Abundant migrant; locally abundant summer resident.

EARLIEST SPRING DATE—April 14, 1946. AVERAGE—May 2.

LATEST FALL DATE—November 23, 1947. AVERAGE (of 13 October dates)—October 6.

HABITAT AND DISTRIBUTION—This is a bird of the deciduous woodlands, one of its nesting requirements being a forest floor well covered with leaf litter. Generally and well distributed throughout the region wherever suitable cover for nesting exists.

Read (1853a:407) says of the ovenbird that it is "not abundant" here. Assuming the correctness of this statement, the species seems to have undergone a remarkable increase in numbers during the last century. Although varying in numbers considerably from year to year, its present abundance here may be inferred from several careful breeding bird population studies made over a period of years in the region. B. P. Bole, Jr. found 15 pairs nesting in a 75-acre tract of forest on Little Mountain in 1939; Harold E. Wallin found 20 pairs nesting in a 50-acre tract at Brecksville in 1946; A. B. Williams found 15 pairs nesting in a 39-acre tract at the Holden Arboretum in 1937, and 25 pairs nesting in a 65-acre tract at North Chagrin in 1947.

NESTING—On the ground, under a dome of leaf litter raised up by the bird. Nest site often well concealed by herbaceous growth. From a study of many nesting records in the region, it is evident that nest construction is generally under way by the middle of May, eggs usually 5, young out of nest by July 10. If first attempts are unsuccessful, subsequent nesting is the rule.

NEWFOUNDLAND OVENBIRD—Seiurus aurocapillus furvior Batchelder

STATUS—Rare migrant.

Our only record of this northeastern form of the ovenbird in the Cleveland region is a specimen in the Fish and Wildlife Service collection in the U. S. National Museum, taken by E. R. Kalmbach, at Painesville, September 17, 1918.

GRINNELL'S WATERTHRUSH—Seiurus noveboracensis notabilis Ridgway

STATUS—Not uncommon migrant; uncommon summer resident.

EARLIEST SPRING DATE—April 15, 1937. AVERAGE—May 7.

LATEST FALL DATE—October 6, 1946. AVERAGE—September 17.

Since it is practically impossible to distinguish this western subspecies from the eastern form (*S. n. noveboracensis*) in the field, and probably all sight records reported for this region refer to *notabilis*, we are including all local sight records of the "northern water-thrush" under this heading. Of the 5 migrant specimens in the collections of the CMNH taken in Ohio, all are *notabilis*. On this basis John W. Aldrich says that "this must be the common migrant as well as the breeding form of this species in this State." (Aldrich 1934:100).

HABITAT AND DISTRIBUTION—Swamp and bog forests and boggy wooded margins of ponds are this bird's preferred habitat. It has been reported during the nesting season at Bradley-Everett Bog (southwest of Burton in Geauga County), Aurora Pond, Solon Bog, South Bog (Geauga County), and Aurora Bog. Five specimens were collected at Solon Bog May 8, 1935, 2 in Mayfield Heights May 14, 1934, 1 in Lakewood May 1, 1930, 1 in North Olmsted April 24, 1925, and 1 killed by striking the Terminal Tower in downtown Cleveland September 7, 1933. Additional specimens are one obtained at Bradley Pond June 14, 1932, one at Pepper Pike Village May 16, 1935, one at Chesterland August 17, 1935, and one at Aurora Pond May 10, 1922.

NESTING—In the course of his studies of the ecology of northern Ohio bogs from 1932 to 1938, John W. Aldrich reported this bird during the breeding season at Bradley-Everett Bog in 1932 and

1934. He found it nesting in the bog forest at the north end of Aurora Pond in 1937 and 1938. From 1 to 4 individuals, including 1 juvenile, were found at Solon Bog May 5 to July 21, 1934, and 1 pair with young just out of the nest June 4, 1937, in a 50-acre tract of bog forest there. One was noted at South Bog May 9, 1934.

During the course of his studies of the breeding birds of a 20-acre tract of swamp forest and bog near Aurora, Carl F. Hamann discovered 3 pairs of these birds in 1946 and 2 pairs in 1947. Nests were found as follows: May 17, 1947, nest, 5 eggs in hollow of low, moss-covered stump in swamp, both adults present. On May 27 conditions were the same. June 4, 1947, nest, 4 eggs, in hole at base of dead stump in same swamp.

LOUISIANA WATERTHRUSH—Seiurus motacilla (Vieillot)

STATUS—Not uncommon migrant; not uncommon summer resident.

EARLIEST SPRING DATE—March 31, 1929. AVERAGE—April 16.

LATEST FALL DATE—October 18, 1942. AVERAGE—September 18.

HABITAT AND DISTRIBUTION—The deep, cool, wooded ravines of the tributary streams of the Chagrin, Cuyahoga and Rocky Rivers are the favorite haunts of this bird. Here, water is usually trickling over the shales which form the ravine bottoms, tree roots often lie exposed, and the loose humus of the fern-decorated banks is damp and rich. The species is well distributed throughout the region wherever such habitats are available.

NESTING—On the ground, on the side of a ravine not far from the bottom, the nest is tucked under a bunch of ferns, beneath an exposed tree root, or under a mound of dead leaves raised up by the bird. April 15, nest under construction. May 11, nest, 6 eggs. May 16, nest, 5 eggs, hatched May 22. May 16, nest, 3 eggs. June 1, nest, 4 young about 1 week old. June 4, nest "full of young birds". June 8 (a second nest), 2 eggs, 1 newly hatched young; eggs hatched next day; all young left nest June 17. June 13, adult feeding young in nest. June 16, adult feeding young in nest. June 20, young birds out of nest following adults about.

KENTUCKY WARBLER—Oporornis formosus (Wilson)

STATUS—Rare and accidental migrant.

With one exception, all of the recent records of the occurrence of this more southern species in our region are for individual birds observed during the month of May. Years covered are between 1913 and 1943, 9 records in all, made by 6 different observers.

EARLIEST DATE—May 3, 1913 and 1942. LATEST—May 28, 1924.

There is a record of a singing male observed in the Abram's Creek ravine June 26, 1944, by Owen Davies.

HABITAT AND DISTRIBUTION—Locations where the bird has been reported are Gates Mills, Twinsburg, Wade Park, Shaker Lakes, Abram's Creek.

NESTING—Dr. Kirtland (1874a:170) mentions this species as nesting in the vicinity of Cleveland prior to 1852, and is quoted by Read (1853a:423) to the effect that "a few spend the entire summer with us." There is no recent nesting record, however.

CONNECTICUT WARBLER—Oporornis agilis (Wilson)

STATUS—Uncommon migrant.

EARLIEST SPRING DATE—May 3, 1942. AVERAGE—May 10. LATEST —May 31, 1924, 1925, 1940, 1945, 1947.

EARLIEST FALL DATE—August 13, 1941. AVERAGE—September 12. LATEST—October 12, 1948.

HABITAT AND DISTRIBUTION—On migration usually found in swampy or humid areas, often in deep woodlands and usually near the ground.

MOURNING WARBLER—Oporornis philadelphia (Wilson)

STATUS—Uncommon migrant.

EARLIEST SPRING DATE—May 3, 1931 and 1941. AVERAGE—May 15. LATEST—June 2, 1940.

EARLIEST FALL DATE — August 13, 1946. AVERAGE—September 7. LATEST—October 20, 1946.

An unusual record is that of a male and female flushed from the ground, as though from a nest, in Stebbin's Gulch, June 20, 1947, by B. P. Bole, Jr.

HABITAT AND DISTRIBUTION—On migration usually seen in small trees and shrubbery in more or less open places, and particularly about water. Many records for Shaker Lakes and Gordon Park, and east to Gates Mills and Fairport. Records from western sections are from Lakewood, Rocky River and Avon-on-the-Lake.

NORTHERN COMMON YELLOWTHROAT—Geothlypis trichas brachidactyla (Swainson)

STATUS—Common migrant; locally common summer resident.

EARLIEST SPRING DATE—April 15, 1945. AVERAGE—May 4.

LATEST FALL DATE—November 12, 1931. AVERAGE—October 10.

HABITAT AND DISTRIBUTION—Wherever a wet swale or marshy spot occurs, either along the edges of streams or ponds, or in overgrown upland meadows where vegetation is rank, there it is likely that the singing of these birds will proclaim their presence. Well distributed throughout the region.

NESTING—On or near the ground, usually in the midst of clumps of weedy grasses or other such vegetation. May 27, nest, 4 eggs. June 9, nest in clump of goldenrod about 1 inch above ground level, 5 eggs; June 13, 4 young, 1 egg; June 18, nest empty. June 15, nest, 4 eggs. June 18, adults feeding 4 young out of nest. July 29, adults feeding 4 nearly fledged young.

YELLOW-BREASTED CHAT—Icteria virens virens (Linnaeus)

STATUS—Uncommon migrant; not uncommon summer resident.

EARLIEST SPRING DATE—April 26, 1942. AVERAGE—May 9.

LATEST FALL DATE—October 9, 1945. AVERAGE—September 27.

HABITAT AND DISTRIBUTION—Prefers thickets, overgrown brushy clearings, tangled shrubbery, overgrown pastures and abandoned fields. Although Read (1853a:375) says the chat nests here "in limited numbers", it has, until quite recently, hardly appeared in our records. During the last few years it has been recorded more often, and it seems to be increasing in numbers. It seems to be more frequently found east and south of Cleveland than west, although there are a few records from the Rocky River Valley and Elyria.

143

NESTING—May 16, nest 4 feet up, 1 egg. May 30, nest, 3 eggs. June 12, nest in thick beech sapling growth, 3 eggs. June 22, nest about 4 feet from ground in tangle of bushes, containing 1 young, 1 unhatched egg. June 22, nest, 3 eggs.

HOODED WARBLER—Wilsonia citrina (Boddaert)

STATUS—Not uncommon to locally abundant summer resident in eastern and southern wooded portions of the region; seldom migrates north of Great Lakes.

EARLIEST SPRING DATE—April 24, 1948. AVERAGE—May 7.

LATEST FALL DATE—October 5, 1946. AVERAGE—September 23.

HABITAT AND DISTRIBUTION—The cool, humid, dark beech-maple forest, particularly along ravine edges, although to a lesser degree moist upland woods, is the preferred habitat of this warbler. In the Cleveland region the bulk of the hooded warbler population is in the Chagrin River drainage area where many wooded gullies and ravines create an environment apparently much to the bird's liking. To a lesser degree the valley of the Cuyahoga and its tributaries are also occupied. In the last few years the bird has appeared in the Rocky River drainage also, and is apparently extending its range locally westward. West of the valley of Rocky River, however, there are only a few scattering records. There is a single record "4 miles west of Cleveland" where a nest with 3 young was found June 19, 1926 (Moulton 1927). From Elyria F. M. Phelps writes that the hooded warbler is an "uncommon summer resident near Elyria. It was unknown as a nesting species here until 1947, when it appeared in the northern part of Ely Woods, within the City of Elyria. First noted singing May 23, late in June, twice in July, and also in early August. Two pairs were present throughout the nesting season, but no systematic search for the nest was made." The only other Ohio record west of Cleveland for a nesting pair appears to be that reported by Campbell (1940:152) for Lucas County, June 15, 1930. It is estimated by A. B. Williams, who has made an intensive study of this species in northern Ohio over a period of 20 years, that probably 5000 pairs of hooded warblers regularly nest in the Rocky, Cuyahoga, Chagrin and Grand River drainage systems.

NESTING—The hooded warbler is an abundant breeding species on Little Mountain, throughout the Chagrin Valley and its tributary gorges, and in the Brecksville and Hinckley Reservations, as determined by breeding population studies conducted over a period of years by B. P. Bole, Jr. on Little Mountain; Arthur B. Williams at the Holden Arboretum, Hinckley, and North Chagrin; and Harold E. Wallin at Brecksville. From these studies it appears that in a 65-acre tract of beech-maple-hemlock forest from 9 to 16 pairs nested annually from 1932 to 1948; in a 75-acre tract of pine-hemlock forest from 7 to 12 pairs nested annually from 1935 to 1939; in a 39-acre tract of beech-maple-hemlock forest from 6 to 9 pairs nested annually from 1937 to 1940; in a 50-acre tract of oak-hickory forest, with beech-maple in the ravines, from 4 to 6 pairs nested annually from 1943 to 1948.

From a study of more than 100 nesting records in the region, it appears that the hooded warbler's nest is placed, on the average, about 26 inches from the ground (measured to rim of nest). Favorite locations are in sugar maple seedlings, beech suckers, or grape tangles. Nests are well camouflaged and screened by surrounding foliage. Nest construction usually begins by the third week in May. Eggs 3 to 4, laid usually during last week in May. Incubation period 12 days. Young in nest 12 days. Nesting activities are prolonged in cases where first or second attempts are unsuccessful.

WILSON'S WARBLER—Wilsonia pusilla pusilla (Wilson)

STATUS—Common migrant.

EARLIEST SPRING DATE — April 24, 1948. AVERAGE — May 11.

LATEST—June 2, 1945 and 1946.

EARLIEST FALL DATE—August 23, 1942. AVERAGE—September 4.

LATEST—October 3, 1945.

There is an unusual record for July 4, 1938, on Little Mountain; and another for July 28, 1946.

HABITAT AND DISTRIBUTION—On migration found almost anywhere in bushes or trees, often near water, and usually not high up.

CANADA WARBLER—Wilsonia canadensis (Linnaeus)

STATUS—Common migrant.

EARLIEST SPRING DATE—April 20, 1948. AVERAGE—May 9. LATEST —June 8, 1936.

EARLIEST FALL DATE — August 8, 1932. AVERAGE — August 17. LATEST—October 26, 1946.

An unusual record is that of a singing male reported for Little Mountain June 20, 1947, by B. P. Bole, Jr.

HABITAT AND DISTRIBUTION—On migration is found usually in trees or shrubs in more open situations; generally distributed throughout the region.

AMERICAN REDSTART—Setophaga ruticilla ruticilla (Linnaeus)

STATUS—Common migrant; common summer resident.

EARLIEST SPRING DATE—April 22, 1945. AVERAGE—May 4.

LATEST FALL DATE—October 17, 1931. AVERAGE (of 15 October dates)—October 8.

HABITAT AND DISTRIBUTION—During migration often seen within the city limits, and in suburban residence areas. Typically a bird of deciduous woodlands of many types, but not entirely confined to forested areas. According to breeding bird population studies made in an oak-hickory forest at Brecksville by Harold E. Wallin in 1947, this was found to be the most abundant nesting species, as many as 17 pairs being recorded nesting in the 50-acre tract under study. Well distributed throughout the region, more common in the eastern and southern sections than in the western.

NESTING—Usually in understory sapling growth within the forest. Nest from 6 to 30 feet up, usually in crotch close to central stem of tree. From a study of numerous nesting records it appears that nest construction is begun about May 15. Eggs 3 to 4. June 5, nest, 4 eggs. Young usually out of nest third week in June. Second attempts are made when first are unsuccessful.

Family PLOCEIDAE (Weaver Finches)

ENGLISH SPARROW—Passer domesticus domesticus (Linnaeus)

STATUS—Abundant permanent resident.

This bird, which technically is not a sparrow, but a weaver finch, probably originating in Africa, was imported from Europe to the United States first in 1850 and 1852. The first importation into Ohio arrived at Cleveland direct from Europe in 1869, consisting of 20 pairs (Jones 1903:221). Dr. Kirtland, writing May 22, 1876, says, "Within the last week the English Sparrow has for the first time visited my premises, five miles west from Cleveland (now 14013 Detroit Avenue, Lakewood), in which city it was first introduced five or six years since and has now become there very numerous." (Christy 1936:89). The rapid spread of the progeny of these first birds in the Cleveland region is set forth by Barrows (1889:221) of the U. S. Department of Agriculture as follows: 1874 Bainbridge, 1875 Strongsville, 1876 Chagrin Falls, 1877 North Royalton, 1878 Brecksville, 1880 Berea, 1881 Mentor, 1883 Wilson's Mills, 1884 Parma.

HABITAT AND DISTRIBUTION—Found throughout the open country about farms and farm buildings, in suburban residence communities about houses, in cities about all sorts of buildings, even the largest. Common in city streets and along country roads, and may even be seen in some numbers about the Cleveland Public Square, where it shares with the pigeons the food that various people provide. Widely distributed throughout the region.

The present abundance of the species may be inferred from breeding bird population studies made at Gates Mills at the Baldwin Bird Research Laboratory in 1939 by S. C. Kendeigh, who found 7 pairs breeding in a 15-acre tract of country estate including several buildings. A similar study made in 1941 in Shaker Heights and Cleveland Heights by R. W. Hill, M. W. Jacoby and A. B. Williams in suburban residence communities totaling 33.4 acres, disclosed a breeding population of 42 pairs, or better than 1 pair per acre. The Christmas Bird Count, conducted by the Kirtland Bird Club January 2, 1949, in a suburban area east of Cleveland 15 miles in diameter, listed 392 English sparrows.

NESTING—Usually about buildings in niches behind blinds, or in cavities, or in holes in trees. Often in nest boxes provided for other birds. Sometimes a large, roughly globular nest, with an entrance

147

at the side, may be built in the branches of a tree close to the main trunk. R. W. Dexter says that juveniles (just off the nest) have been banded by him at Kent from April 10 to September 23, indicating a long nesting season. May 13, nest, 4 eggs. June 26, 10 nests with young about ready to leave.

Family ICTERIDAE (Meadowlarks, Blackbirds, and Troupials)

BOBOLINK—Dolichonyx oryzivorus (Linnaeus)

STATUS—Common migrant; common summer resident.

EARLIEST SPRING DATE—April 14, 1945. AVERAGE—May 2.

LATEST FALL DATE—October 9, 1948. AVERAGE—September 14.

Read (1853a:319) states that "some years ago it was not to be found on the Reserve. Now most common." Wheaton (1882:352) places its first appearance in Geauga County in 1857.

HABITAT AND DISTRIBUTION—Widely distributed over the region in open and scrubby fields, meadows, and roadsides near open fields.

NESTING—May 20, female gathering nesting materials; May 29, nest, 6 eggs. June 22, nest in meadow, 2 eggs, 2 newly hatched young. June 22, nest in grassy field among coarse grass, daisies and clover, 5 fully feathered young with eyes open. July 11, nest with one young and one infertile egg; adults carrying green caterpillars to young bird about ready to leave nest.

EASTERN MEADOWLARK—Sturnella magna magna (Linnaeus)

STATUS—Common migrant; common summer resident; occasional in winter.

EARLIEST SPRING DATE—February 22, 1921. AVERAGE—March 12.

LATEST FALL DATE—November 24, 1943. AVERAGE—October 31.
Several December records.

HABITAT AND DISTRIBUTION—Open fields and scrub growth over entire region. Population not heavy in any one locality, but birds are widely distributed.

NESTING—Nesting has been observed from April to August. Nests contain 4-5 eggs. Pair seen courting March 15. May 10, nest

148

found under old goldenrod stems in field, 4 eggs. May 20, nest, 4 eggs. May 31, nest, 5 eggs. June 16, nest with 4 young.

WESTERN MEADOWLARK—Sturnella neglecta Audubon

STATUS—Rare summer resident.

A male specimen of this species was collected in Lakewood by S. Hall April 8, 1880 (Stevenson 1931). Frank N. Shankland of Willoughby writes that in May 1938 a western meadowlark appeared on the lawn in front of the Andrews Institute, Willoughby, and stayed about a week. It was recognized by song by Mr. Shankland, who was familiar with it through experience in the west. A more recent record is that of a probable nesting pair at Bath, reported by Charles P. Mountz April 28, 29, 1945, and again in the same field May 12, 1946. Identified by song.

EASTERN REDWING—Agelaius phoeniceus phoeniceus (Linnaeus)

STATUS—Abundant migrant; locally abundant summer resident.

EARLIEST SPRING DATE—February 8, 1948. AVERAGE — February 28. PEAK OF NUMBERS—Early April.

Common until November 15. A few winter, especially in the Rocky River Valley.

HABITAT AND DISTRIBUTION—Redwings breed in colonies, normally in marshes and at the edges of ponds, though often in open fields. In 1945 ten or more pairs nested in the wild mustard in an open field near Elyria. In the spring and fall they congregate in enormous flocks, often being associated with cowbirds or grackles. Well distributed over the region wherever suitable marshy areas are available.

NESTING—The early nests are practically all built in old cattails about 18 inches from the water. Later nests are often found in shrubbery or willows 5 to 6 feet up. One nest at North Chagrin was in the top of a 20 foot sugar maple. From a 5-year study (1943-1947) of the breeding bird population of a 15.3-acre tract, including small pond and margin, Vera Carrothers found from 20 to 40 pairs nesting annually. As many as a dozen nests might be crowded into an area 15 feet square.

From a study of many nesting records it appears that the earliest date for eggs is April 25; average, May 5. Earliest young, May 16; average, May 21. Earliest date for young leaving nest, May 26; average, May 30; latest, July 10. Incubation is 10 or 11 days, and the young stay in the nest the same length of time. Eggs, usually 4.

GIANT REDWING—Agelaius phoeniceus arctolegus Oberholser

STATUS—Rare migrant.

Our only record of this northwestern subspecies for the region is a single specimen in the CMNH collections from Auburn, collected by Emerson Kemsies March 22, 1931 (Aldrich 1932).

ORCHARD ORIOLE—Icterus spurius (Linnaeus)

STATUS—Uncommon migrant; rare summer resident.

EARLIEST SPRING DATE—April 29, 1944. AVERAGE—May 13.

LATEST FALL DATE—September 6, 1943. AVERAGE—September 5.

Apparently this species is decreasing in numbers here of late years. Read (1853a:311) states, "somewhat abundant, but not as abundant as Baltimore Oriole."

HABITAT AND DISTRIBUTION—Seen in city parks, residential districts, old orchards and suburban areas. Formerly frequented fruit orchards close to Lake Erie.

NESTING—Keck (1916:13) mentions the orchard oriole as nesting on a lot adjoining his home on East 126th Street, Cleveland. A. B. Williams recalls seeing a nest of this species with both birds in attendance in an old apple tree at Mentor Headlands, probably in the spring of 1918. Donald L. Newman reported seeing a bird August 4, 1940, at Mentor-on-the-Lake. A specimen was collected at Mentor Headlands June 12, 1935, now in CMNH collection. R. W. Dexter writes, "This species nested in a pine tree in the cemetery at Stow in the summer of 1942. Nest made from fresh green grass. C. P. Mountz banded 2 nestlings in the nest June 22, 1942, and a fledgling from the nest June 28, 1942. Nest in collection of Kent State University." F. M. Phelps, while residing in Lakewood in 1919-1920, found this species nesting in the small pear orchard back of the old Andrews home at Detroit and Andrews

Avenue June 6, 1919, 4 eggs. Phelps also found a nest with 4 eggs about 11 feet up in a pear tree at Bay Village June 12, 1919; and another at Bay Village June 3, 1920, nest, 4 eggs, 15 feet up in an apple tree; and a nest with 5 eggs 18 feet up in an apple tree in an orchard at Oak Point (at mouth of Beaver Creek, west of Lorain) June 6, 1922. This species nested regularly in this orchard several years. F. N. Shankland recalls a nesting pair near the lake shore north of Willoughby in the summer of 1939.

BALTIMORE ORIOLE—Icterus galbula (Linnaeus)

STATUS—Common migrant; common summer resident; accidental in winter.

EARLIEST SPRING DATE—March 24, 1946. AVERAGE—May 1.

LATEST FALL DATE—September 16, 1948. AVERAGE—September 5.

Some unusual dates are the following: January 3, 1927, a male (an injured bird) seen feeding on frozen grapes and berries in a garden in Lakewood (Benedict 1927); April 6 and 27, 1924, a bird reported by Ruth Bradway at Mentor, "evidently" there all winter; March 24, 1946, bird at feeder in Cleveland Heights reported by Mrs. R. G. Grieg; April 4, 1943, a bird observed in Cleveland Heights by Alice Porter.

HABITAT AND DISTRIBUTION — Frequently seen in city parks, suburban areas, along country roads, and woods edges. Generally distributed over the area.

NESTING—The hanging nests are usually suspended well out on branches of trees having rather slender twigs, such as elms and maples. There is one record of a bird nesting in a Norway spruce at Painesville, reported by Doolittle (1937:52) during the summer of 1932. Nesting records are numerous: April 25, female constructing nest 20 feet up in elm; May 2, nest completed. May 11, nest begun, later abandoned, new nest on opposite side of street May 13-15. May 16, two partially completed nests. May 17, female binding first strands of materials for nest on branch of elm 40 feet up. May 18, bird weaving nest in elm overhanging country road. May 27, nest, 5 eggs. May 30, nest in process of construction 20 feet up. June 8, bird incubating in nest in elm. June 17, one juvenile flew from nest in top of 12-foot maple. June 25, female

151

feeding young in nest. July 2, adults feeding 1 young out of nest. Hamann says that a male was observed by him feeding 1 young in a swamp forest in 1947.

RUSTY BLACKBIRD—Euphagus carolinus (Müller)

STATUS—Common migrant.

EARLIEST SPRING DATE — February 12, 1938. AVERAGE—April 9. LATEST—May 9, 1948.

EARLIEST FALL DATE—September 20, 1938. LATEST FALL DATE—December 23, 1928. AVERAGE—October 4.

Flocks of up to 1000 birds reported seen during spring and autumn.

HABITAT AND DISTRIBUTION — Seen commonly near swamps, streams and open fields during migration. Many records from Richmond Beach, Solon Bog, Shaker Lakes, Holden Arboretum and city parks.

BRONZED GRACKLE—Quiscalus quiscula versicolor Vieillot

STATUS—Common migrant; locally common summer resident; occasional in winter.

EARLIEST SPRING DATE—February 4, 1943. AVERAGE—March 4.

LATEST FALL DATE—December 28, 1944. AVERAGE—November 10.

Mentioned by Kirtland (1850) as among birds common to Cleveland at the time of the first surveys (about 1796).

HABITAT AND DISTRIBUTION — During migration the bronzed grackle is seen throughout the region, mainly in residential districts and city parks. They have a habit of forming roosts, as when 1000 roosted in a thicket at Painesville (Doolittle 1919a); and when roosts with numerous individuals were begun before the breeding season was over at Elyria and augmented by females and young later in the season (Dawson 1903:34).

NESTING—Kirtland (1850), writing in the Family Visitor, says, "The Crow Black Bird might be found nesting in almost every hollow and cavity in decaying trees. His habits, in constructing his nest, were different from his kin in the New England States, where it builds its nest exclusively on some fork of a limb of a live tree near its extremity.''

Our recent nesting records are chiefly from Shaker Lakes, where the nests are built mainly in evergreen trees. April 24, birds noted gathering nesting materials. May 4, old bird on nest in eaves trough of house. May 4, 3 nests, old birds incubating; May 14, two nests blown down, one containing 3 young a few days old, the other, 3 eggs. May 10, nest, 5 young. May 17, young out of nest. May 20, two nests in tall pine, young in nest, one out of nest. June 9, nest with young. June 16, flocking.

EASTERN COWBIRD—Molothrus ater ater (Boddaert)

STATUS—Common migrant; common summer resident.

EARLIEST SPRING DATE—February 26, 1948. AVERAGE—March 26.

LATEST FALL DATE—November 30, 1940. AVERAGE—October 31.

The bird has been reported twice in December and once in January.

HABITAT AND DISTRIBUTION — Widely distributed over entire area in nearly all types of habitat.

NESTING—Reported present in most areas where studies of nesting bird populations have been made. This bird habitually deposits its eggs in other birds' nests. From one to three eggs per nest have been found from May 13 to July 26 in nests of other species. Those species of which we have records as thus parasitized in our region are:

Phoebe	Yellow Warbler	English Sparrow
Alder Flycatcher	Chestnut-sided	Redwing
Prairie Horned Lark	Warbler	Scarlet Tanager
Wood Thrush	Ovenbird	Cardinal
Yellow-throated	Louisiana Water-	Indigo Bunting
Vireo	thrush	Red-eyed Towhee
Red-eyed Vireo	Northern Yellow-	Savannah Sparrow
Prothonotary	throat	Slate-colored Junco
Warbler	Yellow-breasted	Chipping Sparrow
Blue-winged Warbler	Chat	Field Sparrow
Black-throated	Hooded Warbler	Swamp Sparrow
Green Warbler	Redstart	Song Sparrow

153

Family THRAUPIDAE (Tanagers)

SCARLET TANAGER—Piranga olivacea (Gmelin)

STATUS—Common migrant; common summer resident.

EARLIEST SPRING DATE—April 18, 1943. AVERAGE—May 3.

LATEST FALL DATE—October 12, 1948. AVERAGE—September 27.

HABITAT AND DISTRIBUTION—This is a bird of wooded areas. It is generally distributed throughout the region in woodlands, and is even sometimes found as a breeding bird in suburban communities where large trees are available. On migration may be seen almost anywhere. The following records from breeding population studies indicate something of the wide distribution and densities of the breeding populations in the region. In a 65-acre tract of beech-maple forest at North Chagrin A. B. Williams found an average of 6.1 pairs nesting annually over a 15-year period from 1932 to 1947. Extremes were 3 pairs in 1940 and 10 pairs in 1934. In a 39-acre tract of beech-maple-hemlock forest at the Holden Arboretum A. B. Williams and M. B. Walters found an average of 3.3 pairs nesting annually over a 5-year period from 1937 to 1941. In a 75-acre tract of white pine-hemlock forest on Little Mountain B. P. Bole, Jr. found an average of 4 pairs nesting annually over a 6-year period from 1933 to 1939. In a 30-acre tract of wet beech-maple woodland at the corner of Cedar Road and Gates Mills Boulevard, Vera Carrothers and Margarette E. Morse found 2 pairs nesting in 1940, 1 pair in 1941. In a 50-acre tract of oak-hickory forest at Brecksville H. E. Wallin found an average of 3.4 pairs nesting annually over a period of 5 years between 1941 and 1947. In a 23-acre tract of swamp forest at Aurora Pond J. W. Aldrich found 1 pair nesting in 1933 and 1 pair in 1937. In a 20-acre tract of swamp forest near Aurora C. F. Hamann found 1 pair nesting in 1946, 1 in 1947.

NESTING—Nest usually placed well up in large tree. Some nesting records are the following: May 29, nest under construction on flat fork of branch of beech tree 20 feet up over park road; June 21, adults feeding young in nest; June 26, young out of nest. June 8, male feeding fully fledged young out of nest. June 18, nest with young several days old. June 22, nest with young being fed by male. June 27, nest with 3 young about half fledged. July 8, nest probably containing young with male in attendance. July 9, male feeding young out of nest. August 8, nest with 3 eggs. August 8, both adults feeding 2 young out of nest.

SUMMER TANAGER—Piranga rubra rubra (Linnaeus)

STATUS—Rare and accidental migrant.

Records of this southern tanager in our region are confined to the following: May 6, 1940, one seen at Shaker Lake by Mr. and Mrs. Malcolm Good; May 8, 1944, a male bird seen in the Cuyahoga Falls gorge by Dr. Warren Towle of Akron; July 10, 1945, a male bird, singing, in Gordon Park, reported by B. P. Bole, Jr. Mr. Bole also says that a specimen of this bird, taken in the region, was included in his father's collection. F. M. Phelps reports seeing a bird of this species May 2, 1949, 5 miles south of Elyria near the Black River.

Family FRINGILLIDAE (Grosbeaks, Finches, Sparrows and Buntings)

EASTERN CARDINAL—Richmondena cardinalis cardinalis (Linnaeus)

STATUS—Common permanent resident.

This species, once uncommon here, has gradually been occupying more and more territory, until now it is one of the most common birds of the region. Its increase in numbers here is well attested by the following reports:

Kirtland (1838:184) wrote that up to about 1834 the cardinal was scarcely known in the Western Reserve, but that within a few years thereafter it had become common, and was a winter resident. In 1913, Herrick, writing in the Cleveland Bird Calendar, Bulletin No. 1, remarked that cardinals were present during the winter of 1912-13 in unusual numbers, "as many as six or eight having been observed in Rockefeller and Wade Parks and in Lakeview Cemetery." On December 27, 1926, H. E. Duer reported counting 26 cardinals in North Olmsted. During a well organized Christmas Bird Count conducted by the Kirtland Bird Club in an area 15 miles in diameter east of Cleveland January 2, 1949, a total of 159 cardinals was reported therein.

HABITAT AND DISTRIBUTION—The cardinal has made itself thoroughly at home in close association with human habitations, and

155

is perhaps more numerous in suburban residence sections than it is in wooded country. It is a bird of the shrubbery and tangled thickets. In forested areas it inhabits grape tangles and brushy locations. It is well distributed over the region.

NESTING—In shrubbery, vines, grape tangles, small thorn or crab trees, or even brambles. Eggs hatching as early as April 30 have been recorded. Three broods are not unusual. Young leaving nest have been recorded as late as September 21.

ROSE-BREASTED GROSBEAK—Pheucticus ludovicianus (Linnaeus)

STATUS — Not uncommon migrant; not uncommon summer resident.

EARLIEST SPRING DATE—April 8, 1948. AVERAGE—May 7.

LATEST FALL DATE—October 10, 1938. AVERAGE—September 17.

HABITAT AND DISTRIBUTION—During the spring migration may be found almost anywhere where there are trees. During the nesting season it frequents open woodlands, woods edges, and overgrown fields. Well distributed throughout the region.

NESTING—Records indicate a wide variety of nesting sites, from 4 feet up in thorn bush, to 100 feet up in large beech. Nest construction begins about May 15. Young in nest May 25. Most breeding bird population studies made in the region including wooded territory record from 1 to 4 pairs as nesting regularly. June 20, 23, female and male observed alternately on nest.

EASTERN BLUE GROSBEAK—Guiraca caerulea caerulea (Linnaeus)

STATUS—Rare and accidental migrant.

The records of the appearance of this southern bird in our region are as follows:

April 29, 1919, one reported by Prof. W. H. Hulme of Western Reserve University seen in Wade Park. May 23, 1925, one reported by Prof. Hulme seen in Joplin's Woods, Willoughby. July 15, 1925, one young male reported by Doolittle (1926) seen at Painesville. May 7, 1926, and May 14, 1929, one reported by Prof. Hulme as seen in Wade Park. May 15, 1933, one male reported by

A. B. Williams as seen in a grape tangle at North Chagrin. July 19, 1933, two reported by B. P. Bole, Jr. and A. B. Williams seen in Rocky River Valley. May 4, 1936, one female reported by R. Frank Kukowitch as seen in shrubbery near West Technical High School Greenhouse, Cleveland, observed for 10 minutes at close range. May 3, 1942, one reported by J. O. McQuown seen in Rocky River Valley. July 12, 1942, a male and a female reported seen near Novelty by C. T. Downer.

HABITAT AND DISTRIBUTION — The birds seen here were all in open situations and the more recent ones, at least, in shrubbery rather than in trees.

INDIGO BUNTING—Passerina cyanea (Linnaeus)

STATUS—Common migrant; common summer resident.

EARLIEST SPRING DATE—April 16, 1944. AVERAGE—May 9.

LATEST FALL DATE—October 17, 1946. AVERAGE—September 22.

HABITAT AND DISTRIBUTION—Generally observed throughout the region during spring migration, but most common in outlying districts such as the Metropolitan Parks, Chagrin River Valley, and Little Mountain. During breeding season inhabits brushy thickets and fields, overgrown fence rows, edges of woodlands, and shrubby borders of country roads.

NESTING—June 5, two nests containing 3 and 4 fresh eggs, both nests situated in coarse weed growth about 18 inches above the ground. June 8, nest in tangle of berry vines and saplings along old fence about 2 feet from ground in maple seedling, nest just completed; June 15, four eggs. June 22, nest in briar bush 6 feet up, 3 young. June 23, nest with 1 egg; June 25, three eggs; July 6, all eggs hatched. July 25, 4 young left nest.

DICKCISSEL—Spiza americana (Gmelin)

STATUS—Rare and accidental migrant; rare summer resident.

This prairie bird, not uncommon in western Ohio, has been recorded several times in our region as follows: April 18, 1920, one seen near Painesville by Doolittle (1920b); summer of 1925, one reported by Carl T. Robertson (Plain Dealer "Outdoor

157

Diary") (Kendeigh 1925:340) ; June 5, 7 ,1945, two seen on each of these dates near Willoughby by F. N. Shankland.

HABITAT AND DISTRIBUTION—Prefers open country and roadside thickets.

NESTING—B. P. Bole, Jr. recalls that a pair of these birds nested at the corner of Sperry Road and Mulberry Road, Kirtland Township, from 1929 to 1940. The birds were frequently seen, and heard singing, and were observed with young. These were seen also by P. N. Moulthrop.

EASTERN EVENING GROSBEAK—Hesperiphona vespertina vespertina (Cooper)

STATUS—Rare and irregular winter visitor.

This species, which breeds in the northwest, was first recorded in our region by Kirtland (1860) in the Ohio Farmer of March 24, 1860, who says: "Early last week a beautiful specimen of a female was secured by Charles Pease, Jr., and on the next day I saw several others of this species."

Jones (1911:60) mentions an "1890-91 visitation" of these birds. It then began to appear in Doolittle's records for Painesville, March 20, 30, 31, 1909; March 13, 16, 1911 (Jones 1911:60) ; January 6, 1914; May 18-20, 1919; and December 22, 1929 (Doolittle 1914; 1919c; 1920c:98; 1930).

It was recorded at Gates Mills April 25, 1925 (W. H. Hulme), and at Lakewood April 25, 1930 (specimen). More recently 4 birds were reported at Mentor March 14, 1937 (M. E. Morse) ; a flock near Painesville November 10, 1937 (Walker 1938a:152) ; two birds in Rocky River Valley November 2, 1941 (Rollin C. Dyke) ; six birds in the Chagrin Valley March 7, 1942 (Winifred Goodsell).

The 1945-46 incursion of large numbers of these spectacular birds will long be remembered by Cleveland bird students. Reported first on November 18, 1945, the last date recorded was May 12, 1946. During the intervening time the birds were frequently seen and reported in numbers ranging from 1 to 125. They regularly visited feeding stations where they showed a decided preference for sunflower seeds.

In 1947 two birds were seen January 18, 19, 26, at Silver Lake (near Cuyahoga Falls) by C. F. Gibbs; 1 seen at a feeding station in Aurora by Carl F. Hamann February 21; 4 reported at Kent May 18 by Ralph W. Dexter.

From the above records it will be seen that the extreme dates between which evening grosbeaks have been recorded as visitors here are November 2 and May 20.

HABITAT AND DISTRIBUTION—The appearance of evening grosbeaks seems to be unpredictable. Although found in woodlands at North Chagrin and Rocky River, they have appeared more frequently in open situations, about human habitations and even in suburban residence communities. So far as our records go, the bird has not been observed in our region west of the valley of Rocky River.

EASTERN PURPLE FINCH—Carpodacus purpureus purpureus (Gmelin)

STATUS—Not uncommon migrant; uncommon summer resident.

EARLIEST MARCH DATE—March 4, 1945. AVERAGE—March 12.

EARLIEST SEPTEMBER DATE—September 2, 1934 and 1943. AVERAGE OF LAST OCTOBER DATES—October 16.

While we have records of occurrence here for every month in the year, there appears to be a peak of numbers in April and May and another in late September and October. Numbers decrease in November and December, with still smaller numbers in January and February. Often no winter records.

HABITAT AND DISTRIBUTION—Has some preference for coniferous trees, but in spring feeds on the buds and new seeds of deciduous trees, and in autumn on weed seeds and the fruit of evergreens, birch, and ironwood. Migrates generally through the region, records coming from the various Metropolitan Parks, Wade Park, Shaker Lakes, and other similar locations.

NESTING—Dr. Kirtland (1874a:170) says: "The Purple Finch . . . visits our gardens and grounds in numerous flocks, every season, early in July, and remains here till the ensuing spring. The young, at their first appearance, still retain much down about their plumage, and can not have been long absent from their nests."

This species has been found to nest east of Cleveland at South Euclid, Gates Mills, and principally, Little Mountain. The first

159

recorded nest was found on May 18, 1911, at Stop 18, South Euclid, by James (Cleveland Bird Calendar No. 2, 1911) in a small recently planted spruce tree, and contained 4 fresh eggs. In 1925 at Gates Mills Kendeigh discovered a nest with 4 eggs on June 20. The nest was 18 feet from the ground in the top of a blue spruce on the front lawn of the Baldwin estate. This nest and eggs are in the CMNH collections. At Gates Mills on June 26, 1933, a female carrying a fully developed egg was collected by Aldrich (1934: 100). Again at Little Mountain in 1937 one pair was found nesting by Bole (1937:384). The species has been recorded at Little Mountain during the months of June and July since that time, and nesting may be presumed to have continued. Doolittle (1917b:162) observed a singing male at Painesville from the end of June to July 11, 1917. On July 28 and August 3, 1948, Hamann observed 3 individuals of this species whose behaviour indicated a small family.

CANADIAN PINE GROSBEAK—Pinicola enucleator leucura (Müller)

STATUS—Rare and irregular visitor.

Dr. Kirtland (1860) records one taken at Rockport (now Lakewood) in the winter of 1859-60. From 1915 to 1947 there are 14 records of the occurrence of this bird in the region. The earliest of these is November 19, 1933. There are 5 December records, 1 January, 1 February, 3 March, 1 April, and 2 May, the latest being May 17, 1930. Mrs. Francis Sherwin observed 3 of these birds feeding in dogwood and crab apple trees at Waite Hill March 5, 1944. She says "they were so tame I almost touched one."

HABITAT AND DISTRIBUTION — Usually prefer localities where there are coniferous trees, but in our region may be found in deciduous woods also. Have been reported from Painesville, Little Mountain, North Chagrin, Mentor, Willoughby, Shaker Lakes, Wade Park, Brecksville, Cleveland, and Lakewood.

COMMON REDPOLL—Acanthis flammea flammea (Linnaeus)

STATUS—Common to uncommon winter visitor.

EARLIEST FALL DATE—November 24, 1943.

LATEST SPRING DATE—April 27, 1947.

The incursions of the redpoll from its northern habitat are sporadic. They may be abundant one year and infrequently noted the next. They fly about in close flocks, sometimes of 25-150 individuals, and may at times be associated with the goldfinch, whose feeding habits are similar. Kirtland (1838:183) states that a large flock stayed in his garden for three winter months in the years 1836-7, and (1860) that in the winter of 1859-60 very few were seen.

HABITAT AND DISTRIBUTION—Most recorded observations come from the eastern part of the region. Most commonly seen in open country where it forages for weed seeds, but it also enjoys feasting on birch and hemlock seeds. It is generally seen in rural and suburban sections, and also in the Metropolitan Parks and Shaker Lakes.

NORTHERN PINE SISKIN—Spinus pinus pinus (Wilson)

STATUS—Uncommon migrant; uncommon winter visitor.

EARLIEST FALL DATE—September 25, 1938.

LATEST SPRING DATE—May 24, 1942.

There is a distinct increase in numbers observed in May, whereas fall migration seems to be more extended, occupying October and November. Winter records seem to be only casual.

HABITAT AND DISTRIBUTION — Practically all records for this species are from the sections east of Cleveland, such as Willoughby, Painesville, Mentor, Chesterland, the Metropolitan Parks, and Shaker Lakes. It often associates with the goldfinch and the purple finch, feeding in the trees in company with these species.

EASTERN GOLDFINCH—Spinus tristis tristis (Linnaeus)

STATUS—Common migrant; common permanent resident.

HABITAT AND DISTRIBUTION—Conspicuous during the breeding season because of its bright plumage and characteristic song, but less obvious in the winter months when it assumes its less brilliant coat and travels about in roving bands through the countryside, generally feeding on weed seeds. As many as 50 individuals (1940) have been observed during a Christmas Bird Count. Observed

161

generally over the region in open country, usually frequenting shrubby and weedy areas in the city and suburbs, but occasionally in wooded sections. Most records come from outlying country, west, south, and east of Cleveland, Metropolitan Parks, Fairport. Breeding pairs have been noted in censuses at Fairport Harbor (sand dunes), Aurora (marsh and swamp), Rocky River Valley (flood plain forest), and North Chagrin (pond and border).

NESTING—Of six nests observed, the earliest was completed July 16, others discovered August 3, 5, 15; three nests apparently contained young August 13, 15 and 26. July 18, nest in viburnum bush in marsh 8 feet up; July 29, female incubating 4 eggs. July 31, nest in brushy area with 5 slightly incubated eggs, 4½ feet up in elm sapling. August 8, female deposited first nesting material; August 11, nest completed, 1 egg laid; August 12, second egg laid; August 13, third egg laid; August 14, fourth egg laid, bird remained on nest; August 15, fifth egg laid and incubation begun; August 27, 28, eggs hatched at intervals for 2 days; September 11, young birds left nest. September 14, nest with 4 eggs.

EASTERN RED CROSSBILL—Loxia curvirostra minor (Brehm)

STATUS—Rare and occasional winter visitor.

EARLIEST FALL DATE—October 25, 1941.

LATEST SPRING DATE—May 30, 1920.

Wheaton (1879b:62), commenting on the presence of this species near Columbus in the summer of 1879, says: "I have since learned that the Red Crossbill has remained during the season in the vicinity of Cleveland in considerable numbers, and it is reported to have nested there."

The appearance of the red crossbill here in recent years seems to have followed a 10 or 11 year cycle. They were here in numbers in 1920; in 1931 (November 9, 1931 to January 4, 1932); and in 1940 (December 1, 1940 to May 18, 1941). Three were seen October 25, 1941, at Waite Hill by W. Earl Godfrey. A single bird (female) was reported seen June 16, 1942, in a hemlock tree at North Chagrin (Don Eckelberry).

HABITAT AND DISTRIBUTION—Crossbills usually travel in small flocks of from 15 to 40 individuals, and may be looked for in coniferous trees where they feed upon the seeds, tearing the cones apart in the process. They also feed on the seeds of the tulip tree and the buds of other deciduous trees such as the red maple. Our records come from North Chagrin, Waite Hill, Willoughby, Little Mountain and Holden Arboretum.

WHITE-WINGED CROSSBILL—Loxia leucoptera leucoptera Gmelin

STATUS—Rare and infrequent winter visitor.

Wheaton (1882:318) states that this bird was collected at Willoughby in 1861. Present records are for the years 1940 and 1941, principally the latter, when several small flocks of 30 to 100 birds were observed at North Chagrin on February 16 and 23 (Walters). A flock of 50-75 was also seen in Joplin's Woods (Willoughby) on February 16, 1941 (Hill). Fifteen were seen at North Chagrin January 17, 1943 (Sweeney), and four at Willoughby March 16, 1941 (Skaggs). Its appearance in this region is unpredictable.

RED-EYED TOWHEE—Pipilo erythrophthalmus erythrophthalmus (Linnaeus)

STATUS—Common migrant; common summer resident; common to uncommon winter resident.

AVERAGE DATE OF SPRING ARRIVAL—March 21.

AVERAGE DATE OF FALL DEPARTURE—November 5.

On Christmas Bird Counts from one to as many as 30 towhees have been observed, and during the months of January and February single birds, as well as groups of 4 to 6 birds, have often been reported.

Definite migration begins in March, and from the middle of the month to the first days of April the bird apparently becomes established in its breeding territory.

HABITAT AND DISTRIBUTION—Inhabits brushy fields and borders, especially the edges of woods where there is an abundance of leaf litter, through which it searches for its food. Also commonly found in brushy, swampy areas and openings of woodlands. Commonly observed in the Metropolitan Parks, along wooded drives and ravines in the suburbs, usually nesting in outlying parts of the region.

NESTING—Nest usually built on or near the ground at the base of a small tree, bush, or herbaceous plant. May 5, nest construction begun. May 14, nest on ground tucked under broad leaf of skunk cabbage, contained 4 eggs. May 14, nest, 2 eggs. May 17, nest with 1 young about 4 days old. May 22, nest close to base of small maple sapling in woods, 3 eggs. June 7, 3 young in nest at base of small tree. June 7, nest, 4 eggs; June 15, young day or so old. June 12, nest, 4 eggs in small red cedar 2 feet from ground; June 19, still 4 eggs; June 26, four young half feathered; July 3, nest vacant. July 10, nest, 1 egg.

LARK BUNTING—Calamospiza melanocorys Stejneger

STATUS—Rare and accidental migrant.

There is a specimen of this western prairie species, an immature male, in the collection of the CMNH. This bird was picked up at South Euclid September 6, 1944, by M. B. Skaggs (1945), and identified by H. C. Oberholser and W. Earl Godfrey. Normally a bird of the Rocky Mountain and Great Plains area, there are few records of its occurrence east of the Mississippi River.

EASTERN SAVANNAH SPARROW—Passerculus sandwichensis savanna (Wilson)

STATUS—Common migrant; uncommon summer resident.

EARLIEST SPRING DATE—March 8, 1930. AVERAGE—April 13.

LATEST FALL DATE—November 5, 1922. AVERAGE—October 1.

HABITAT AND DISTRIBUTION—Prefers open fields and abandoned pastures. During migration it concentrates in fields adjoining ponds and streams. Well distributed throughout the region in its favorite haunts. The savannah sparrow appears in several studies of breeding bird populations made in the region, but always as single pairs, even in areas as large as 40 acres. This would indicate a very sparse breeding population.

NESTING—On the ground in open scrubby fields. May 10, nest, 4 eggs. May 13, nest, 4 eggs. June 6, nest in slight depression in ground, 3 fully feathered young and 1 unhatched egg. June 10, nest, 2 eggs. June 12, nest, 2 eggs. June 20, nest in cup-shaped cavity on small hummock of earth, 5 eggs; June 29, 2 eggs hatched;

June 30, third egg hatched; July 1, remaining 2 eggs had hatched; July 5, 5 young, eyes open; July 6, nest empty. July 18, 2 nests, 3 eggs in each.

LABRADOR SAVANNAH SPARROW—Passerculus sandwichensis labradorius Howe

STATUS—Rare and accidental migrant.

One specimen of this race of the savannah sparrow, which breeds in Labrador and Newfoundland, taken in our region, is in the CMNH collections. It is a female, collected at Strongsville October 5, 1935.

CHURCHILL SAVANNAH SPARROW—Passerculus sandwichensis oblitus Peters and Griscom

STATUS—Rare and accidental migrant.

Two specimens of this race of the savannah sparrow, which breeds in northern Minnesota, the west side of Hudson Bay, and in central Quebec, taken in our region are in the CMNH collections. They are a male and a female, both collected at Richmond Beach May 3, 1938.

EASTERN GRASSHOPPER SPARROW—Ammodramus savannarum pratensis (Vieillot)

STATUS—Common migrant; locally common summer resident.

EARLIEST SPRING DATE—March 23, 1929. AVERAGE—April 19.

LATEST FALL DATE—November 8, 1948. AVERAGE—October 10.

HABITAT AND DISTRIBUTION—Prefers open fields and meadows largely devoid of trees. Well distributed in such locations throughout the region. It appears in a number of breeding bird population studies made in the area, never in large numbers. In 5 different locations totaling 241 acres in all, studies conducted from 1936 to 1941 by Ralph A. O'Reilly, Jr., P. N. Moulthrop, A. B. Williams, C. H. Knight, and M. B. Skaggs, disclosed 26 pairs of grasshopper sparrows nesting.

NESTING—On the ground in open fields, usually well concealed by clumps of grass or weeds. We have no local nesting data.

WESTERN HENSLOW'S SPARROW—Passerherbulus henslowii henslowii (Audubon)

STATUS—Common migrant; locally abundant summer resident.

EARLIEST SPRING DATE—April 5, 1942. AVERAGE—April 27.

LATEST FALL DATE—October 23, 1948. AVERAGE—September 17.

HABITAT AND DISTRIBUTION—Prefers weedy overgrown meadows and scrubby open fields. Well distributed in such locations throughout the region.

NESTING—On the ground, well concealed by clumps of grass or weeds. There is a tendency to nest in colonies, and to change nesting locations from one season to another. A good illustration of this tendency is shown in the study of a 44-acre tract of open field at the corner of SOM Center Road and Cedar Road, Pepper Pike Village, made by Ralph A. O'Reilly, Jr. In 1936 he found 2 pairs of Henslow's sparrows nesting in this area; in 1937, 19 pairs; in 1938, none. In a similar study made by C. H. Knight on a 40-acre tract bordering on Sulgrave Road, Shaker Heights, in 1939, 11 pairs were found nesting. May 29, nest, 4 eggs. July 11, adult feeding 1 young bird out of nest.

NELSON'S SHARP-TAILED SPARROW—Ammospiza caudacuta nelsoni (Allen)

STATUS—Rare fall migrant.

The collections of the CMNH contain one specimen of this race of the sharp-tailed sparrow from our region. This particular bird was killed September 22, 1931, by striking the Terminal Tower in downtown Cleveland, apparently a casualty of the fall migration.

Since this and the following form are practically indistinguishable in the field, and the migration routes of both seem to coincide here; and since we have no way of telling which race occurs here most frequently, we include under this heading all the records of "sharp-tailed sparrow" or "Nelson's sharp-tailed sparrow" which we have. They are as follows:

September 19, 1938, Aurora Pond (Aldrich); September 23, 1945, Cleveland (Carrothers, Godfrey, Hill); September 24, 1941, North Chagrin pond (A. B. Williams); September 29, 1931, Rich-

mond Beach (Aldrich) ; October 4, 1942, Corning Lake (Godfrey) ;
October 4, 1947, White City (Morse, Piskac) ; October 26, 1919,
Painesville (Doolittle 1920a :66).

HABITAT AND DISTRIBUTION—Usually found here about the
marshy edges of ponds, or among the sand dunes of the Lake Erie
beaches.

JAMES BAY SHARP-TAILED SPARROW—Ammospiza cauda-cuta altera Todd

STATUS—Rare fall migrant.

The collections of the CMNH contain one specimen of this race
of the sharp-tailed sparrow from our region. This bird was collected by John W. Aldrich (1936a :99) September 20, 1931, at
Richmond Beach. Since we have no way of knowing whether this
or the preceding race of the sharp-tailed sparrow may occur here
most frequently, all records of sharp-tailed sparrows reported in
our region are presented together under the previous heading.
Apparently the migration routes of the two races (at least in fall)
may coincide in our region.

EASTERN VESPER SPARROW—Pooecetes gramineus gramineus (Gmelin)

STATUS—Common migrant; common summer resident.

EARLIEST SPRING DATE—March 2, 1946. AVERAGE—April 2.

LATEST FALL DATE—November 12, 1938. AVERAGE—October 13.

There is a record of 1 bird seen January 1, 1904 (Jones
(1904b :113).

HABITAT AND DISTRIBUTION—Prefers open fields or abandoned
pastures. Often seen on unpaved country roads or about sand
dunes on Lake Erie shore. Well distributed throughout the region.
In its choice of nesting locations the vesper sparrow, only to a
lesser degree than the song sparrow, ranges through all of the
typical habitats except woodlands.

NESTING—On the ground in quite open locations. April 26, nest,
3 eggs. May 7, nest, 4 eggs. May 14, nest, 4 young. May 18, nest,
4 eggs. June 18, nest, 4 eggs. July 15, nest "full of young".

EASTERN LARK SPARROW—Chondestes grammacus grammacus (Say)

STATUS—Rare and accidental migrant.

We have but 6 records for this western species in our region: April 27, 1940 (Bohn); April 28, 1882 (Ingersoll 1882); May 5, 1940 (Aldrich); August 18, 1946 (Dobbins); October 13, 1940 (McQuown) (3 birds); October 17, 1935 (O'Reilly).

HABITAT AND DISTRIBUTION — Prefers open weedy fields and abandoned pastures. Locations from which it has been reported are Gordon Park, Cleveland, White City, Rocky River, and Cleveland Heights.

BACHMAN'S SPARROW—Aimophila aestivalis bachmanii (Audubon)

STATUS—Rare and accidental migrant.

Doolittle (1914), reporting on the Bachman's sparrow, says that he first observed it in September 1909 near Painesville, and that he had seen it in the same locality each year since. Last date seen, September 22, 1913. On May 2, 1944, one was reported seen at Shaker Lake by W. Earl Godfrey. Another was reported seen May 1, 3, 6 and 8, 1949, near Kent, by Vernon Weingart.

SLATE-COLORED JUNCO—Junco hyemalis hyemalis (Linnaeus)

STATUS—Common migrant; common winter visitor; rare and extremely localized summer resident.

EARLIEST FALL DATE—September 5, 1942. AVERAGE DATE OF ARRIVAL—September 24.

LATEST SPRING DATE—June 3, 1931. AVERAGE DATE OF DEPARTURE—May 1.

Rather regular June, July records. A common winter visitor, as confirmed by the 1947 Christmas Bird Count, when 612 were counted December 27 in an area east of Cleveland 15 miles in diameter.

HABITAT AND DISTRIBUTION—Well distributed over the region, but most common in suburban and rural districts where it frequents brushy woods and borders and the previous year's culti-

168

vated fields. Commonly travels in flocks of 5 to 20 individuals. Regularly seen at feeding stations throughout the region.

NESTING—This species is mentioned by Kirtland (1838:183) as follows: "The lead-colored snow bird which is seen in such numbers during the winter, does not forsake the State entirely during summer. It breeds in great numbers in the dark beech woods of the Connecticut Western Reserve, and with the approach of cold weather gathers about yards and gardens."

The first recent observation of the junco as a probable breeding species in this region was made at Little Mountain on August 21, 1931 (Baird 1932:16). Aldrich (1934:101) reported it also. Later, in a study of the flora and fauna of a 75-acre tract on Little Mountain, B. P. Bole, Jr. listed from 6 to 10 nesting pairs annually from 1935 to 1939. On May 21, 1945, a nest with 4 young apparently two or three days old was discovered near the edge of a deep ravine at Gates Mills; May 27, four young left this nest (Godfrey, A. B. Williams). On June 20, 1947, a nest with 4 eggs was found at Stebbin's Gulch, east of the Holden Arboretum, by B. P. Bole, Jr. On June 20 and 27, 1941, juveniles were observed at North Chagrin by A. B. Williams. It is probable that the junco still nests in some numbers about the cool ravines of the Chagrin River where hemlocks still contribute a northern aspect to the forest, and in other localities where remnants of the northern types of forests persist.

OREGON JUNCO—Junco oreganus (Townsend)

STATUS—Accidental winter visitor.

Only recently has it been realized that there are races of the Oregon junco which could, and probably do, occur occasionally in our region. Usually such birds would be found here associated with flocks of slate-colored juncos or tree sparrows. Lacking specimens for subspecific identification, we use here the species name to indicate a sight record of an Oregon junco seen with a flock of tree sparrows November 9, 1947, north of Akron, by John E. Lieftinck.

EASTERN TREE SPARROW—Spizella arborea arborea (Wilson)

STATUS—Common winter visitor.

EARLIEST FALL DATE—October 1, 1921. AVERAGE—October 22.

LATEST SPRING DATE—May 22, 1938. AVERAGE—April 22.

HABITAT AND DISTRIBUTION—This is a bird of roadside weed patches, open fields, and weedy marshes in winter, often appearing at feeding stations. Flocks numbering from a few to 100 or more birds are a familiar sight in snow-covered fields, feeding upon the seeds of weeds which stand above the surface of the snow. Its abundance may be inferred from the fact that on a Christmas Bird Count covering a territory approximately 15 miles in diameter to the east of Cleveland, conducted by the Kirtland Bird Club December 27, 1947, 570 tree sparrows were reported seen.

EASTERN CHIPPING SPARROW—Spizella passerina passerina (Bechstein)

STATUS—Common migrant; common summer resident.

EARLIEST SPRING DATE—March 13, 1946. AVERAGE—April 14.

LATEST FALL DATE—November 13, 1942. AVERAGE—October 10.

HABITAT AND DISTRIBUTION—Prefers vicinity of human habitations—yards, orchards, farmlands and abandoned fields. Well distributed throughout the region. The density of chipping sparrow populations in favorable locations may be inferred from the study of nesting birds made at the Baldwin Bird Research Laboratory at Gates Mills by Dr. S. C. Kendeigh, where in 15 acres of typical country estate 8 pairs of chipping sparrows were found nesting in 1937, 6 pairs in 1938.

NESTING—The nest is usually built in shrubbery or lower branches of small trees and is usually lined with horsehair. Eggs 3 to 4, rarely 5. May 18, nest in pine 2 feet up, 4 young. May 22, nest, 4 eggs; May 29, 2 young, 2 eggs; June 5, 3 young; June 12, nest empty. May 26, nest 7 feet up in honeysuckle vine, 2 eggs; June 7, eggs hatched; June 17, young left nest. May 28, nest in barberry 12 inches from ground, 4 eggs; June 5, 4 young just beginning to show feathers; June 11, nest empty, 1 young nearby. June 1, nest in honeysuckle vine about 10 feet up, 3 young in nest being fed by adults; June 5, young left nest.

EASTERN FIELD SPARROW—Spizella pusilla pusilla (Wilson)

STATUS—Abundant migrant; locally abundant summer resident.

EARLIEST SPRING DATE—March 5, 1945. AVERAGE—March 30.

LATEST FALL DATE—December 24, 1923. AVERAGE—October 21.

Unusual records are February 19, 1948, and February 22, 1938 (Akers).

HABITAT AND DISTRIBUTION — Frequents old abandoned fields, areas of thorn scrub, and open places generally where grasses, brambles and small trees abound. It is well distributed throughout the region. The density of field sparrow nesting populations in favorable habitats may be inferred from the following studies made over a period of years from 1936 to 1941 by Ralph A. O'Reilly, Jr., Philip N. Moulthrop, Arthur B. Fuller, B. P. Bole, Jr., Isabelle Hellwig, Rollin C. Dike, Ruth Newcomer, Edith Dobbins and H. C. Dobbins in 9 different localities east, west and south of Cleveland, totaling in all 267 acres, largely old abandoned fields or areas of thorn scrub. The highest density was in an area of 23 acres where 24 pairs of field sparrows were found nesting. The lowest was in an area of 44 acres in which 12 pairs were nesting. The total for the combined acreage was 133 pairs, or about 1 pair for every 2 acres. Included in the total acreage, however, were some areas unsuitable to field sparrow nesting requirements.

NESTING—The nest is placed on the ground or near it in low branches of bushes, brambles or scrubby small trees. Eggs 3 to 5. From a study of many nesting records it appears that nesting may begin as early as the latter part of April (April 30, nest, 2 eggs), and may be continued through August (August 19-26, bird incubating 4 eggs).

HARRIS'S SPARROW—Zonotrichia querula (Nuttall)

STATUS—Rare migrant.

There are 5 records of this more westerly migrating species in our region. These are: May 2, 1943 (Mayfield 1943:8); May 13, 1940 (2 birds) (Gaede, Aldrich); May 13, 14, 15, 16, 1934 (probably same bird) (Gilliland); October 9, 1932 (Fuller); October 21, 1931 (Doolittle 1931:225).

HABITAT AND DISTRIBUTION—Usually found in brush and weed patches in open situations. Localities from which the bird has been reported are Cuyahoga Falls, Cleveland, Rockefeller Park, Shaker Heights, Mentor and Painesville.

EASTERN WHITE-CROWNED SPARROW—Zonotrichia leucophrys leucophrys (Forster)

STATUS—Common migrant.

EARLIEST SPRING DATE — April 6, 1941. AVERAGE — April 25. LATEST—May 30, 1945.

EARLIEST FALL DATE — September 21, 1893. LATEST—November 22, 1942.

An unusual record is one at Lakewood June 23, 1945 (Davies). In the winter of 1942-43 a bird of this species was present all winter at a feeding station on Landon Road (Shaker Heights).

HABITAT AND DISTRIBUTION—On migration this bird frequents woods edges, open fields, swamps or low shrubbery in suburban areas. Well distributed throughout the region.

GAMBEL'S WHITE-CROWNED SPARROW—Zonotrichia leucophrys gambelii (Nuttall)

STATUS—Rare and accidental migrant.

Our only records of this western race of the white-crowned sparrow in our region are of two individuals caught and banded by Merit B. Skaggs at South Euclid May 10 and 15, 1941 (Skaggs 1941), and one caught and banded by Skaggs May 20, 1944 (Mayfield 1944:6). The fact that the subspecies may be distinguished from the species in the field only by close scrutiny under the most favorable conditions may indicate that Gambel's sparrows are possibly more numerous in migration here than these records would lead one to believe.

WHITE-THROATED SPARROW—Zonotrichia albicollis (Gmelin)

STATUS—Common migrant; possible rare summer resident.

EARLIEST SPRING DATE — March 7, 1948. AVERAGE — April 23. LATEST—May 25, 1947.

EARLIEST FALL DATE—August 22, 1948. LATEST—November 29, 1930.

172

There are several winter records, among which are the following: December 8 (4), 1946; December 15, 1933; December 17, 1932; December 20 to 31, 1946; December 23, 1931; December 24, 1935; January 16, 1925; February 2, 1929; February 9, 12, 23, 1947.

HABITAT AND DISTRIBUTION—Prefers woods edges, open scrubby fields, weed patches and low shrubbery. Is often found in such places as grapevine tangles and other littered places in the woods. One was observed daily in December 1931 feeding with the English sparrows and pigeons on Cleveland Public Square. During migration it is well distributed throughout the region.

NESTING—An adult with young apparently just out of the nest was reported by B. P. Bole, Jr. in Bratenahl, June 1929, in an area planted with young red pines and hemlocks (Aldrich 1934: 101). A male was seen and heard singing in East Cleveland July 8, 9, 10, 1946, by Merit and Marion Skaggs.

EASTERN FOX SPARROW—Passerella iliaca iliaca (Merrem)

STATUS—Not uncommon migrant.

EARLIEST SPRING DATE—February 21, 1948. AVERAGE—March 25.

LATEST—May 21, 1946.

EARLIEST FALL DATE—August 22, 1948. LATEST—November 29, 1941.

HABITAT AND DISTRIBUTION—During migration frequents open woodlands, woods edges, and fence rows. Frequently comes to feeding stations. Well distributed over the region in suitable habitats during migration.

LINCOLN'S SPARROW—Melospiza lincolnii lincolnii (Audubon)

STATUS—Uncommon migrant.

EARLIEST SPRING DATE — March 30, 1938. AVERAGE — May 16.

LATEST—May 25, 1947.

EARLIEST FALL DATE—August 17, 1946. LATEST—December 8, 1933.

HABITAT AND DISTRIBUTION—Commonly found in marshy areas, river bottomlands, and about pond edges. Well distributed throughout the region during migration.

173

EASTERN SWAMP SPARROW—Melospiza georgiana georgiana (Latham)

STATUS—Common migrant; common summer resident.

EARLIEST SPRING DATE—March 12, 1938. AVERAGE—April 11.

LATEST FALL DATE—December 6, 1947. AVERAGE—October 19.

Unusual winter records are: January 5, 1940; January 11, 1947; January 19, 1939; February 12, 1939; February 23, 1948.

HABITAT AND DISTRIBUTION—Prefers the swampy margins of ponds, bogs and lakes, river marshes and wet meadows. Well distributed throughout the region in such locations. Density of breeding populations may be inferred from the following breeding bird population studies conducted in typical marshland and swamp forest habitats in the region. J. W. Aldrich, in studies conducted at Aurora Pond in an area of 14.6 acres of marshland, found 17 pairs breeding in 1932; 10 pairs in 1933; 14 pairs in 1934—an average of about 1 pair per acre. In a 20-acre tract of red maple-yellow birch swamp forest, Dr. Aldrich found 7 pairs nesting in 1933. In a 33-acre marsh in a bend of the Cuyahoga River located in Cuyahoga Heights, Franklin Jedlicka found 6 pairs nesting in 1937. At Abram's Lake in 1942, George Bing found 4 pairs nesting in a 65-acre tract. At Aurora, in an upland swamp forest, Carl Hamann found 2 pairs nesting in 1946 and 1947 in a 20-acre tract.

NESTING—On the ground in sedges, grasses, bunches of flags in wet meadows or edges of swamps or marshes. May 13, nest in rushes 10 inches from ground, 5 eggs; May 24, 1 egg and 4 young. May 14, beginning nest construction in cattail clump. May 25, nest in arbor vitae 2 feet from ground, 4 eggs. June 25, nest in cattail clump with fresh eggs. June 2, nest, 3 eggs.

WESTERN SWAMP SPARROW—Melospiza georgiana ericrypta Oberholser

STATUS—Rare and accidental visitor.

There is a specimen of this western race of the swamp sparrow in the CMNH collections taken at Aurora Pond April 14, 1930.

MISSISSIPPI SONG SPARROW—Melospiza melodia euphonia Wetmore

STATUS—Abundant migrant; abundant summer resident.

This is the breeding form of the region.

EARLIEST SPRING DATE—While it is difficult to determine the dates of first arrival due to the fact that so many birds winter here, it may be said that the first migrating song sparrows usually arrive in late February, and that the migration reaches its peak about March 10.

LATEST FALL DATE — The heaviest autumn migration usually develops during the last week of October.

Many individuals are regularly recorded throughout the winter. For the years 1943 to 1947 the Christmas Bird Counts, conducted by the Kirtland Bird Club in an area 15 miles in diameter east of Cleveland, have recorded from 8 to 25 song sparrows in late December, the average being 15.

HABITAT AND DISTRIBUTION—While this species seems to have a decided liking for the vicinity of water, it may be found in almost any location except in woodlands. It is a bird of open fields, woods edges, pond and stream margins, farmlands and shrubbery about buildings. It is not uncommon in suburban residence communities. Well distributed throughout the region.

NESTING—On the ground or in low shrubbery or bushes, or in hedges. The song sparrow is found as a nesting bird in all typical habitats from lake beach to forest edge. From a study of many nesting records it appears that nest construction may begin as early as April 29. Usually 4 days are required to finish the nest. Eggs are laid at the rate of one each day thereafter until a total of 4 or 5 is reached. Incubation begins after the laying of the last egg and continues 12 days. It is then about 12 days before the young are ready to leave the nest. Two or three broods may be raised in a season.

It was estimated in 1933 by Arthur B. Williams that along the course of Rocky River from Little Cedar Point (at the juncture of the east and west branches of Rocky River, Village of North Olmsted) almost to the river's mouth, a pair of song sparrows might be found nesting at about every 300 feet where suitable cover was available.

The song sparrow appears in many breeding bird population studies made in the region. Combining 8 of these to make a total of 243 acres (including some acres of water), we find 91 pairs of song sparrows reported as nesting therein. Typical concentrations are those found by Vera Carrothers in a study of an area of 15.3 acres (including 4.5 acres of water) at North Chagrin, where, over a period of 5 years from 1943 to 1947, an average of 10 pairs of song sparrows were found nesting annually; and in a study made by Dr. S. C. Kendeigh at the Baldwin Bird Research Laboratory at Gates Mills in an area of 15 acres of country estate, where over a five year period from 1935 to 1939 an average of 9 pairs of song sparrows were found nesting annually.

LAPLAND LONGSPUR—Calcarius lapponicus lapponicus (Linnaeus)

STATUS—Rare spring, fall and winter visitor.

SPRING DATES include March 3, 1941(1); April 18, 1925(2); May 2(2), and 3(1), 1928.

FALL AND WINTER DATES range from September 26 (1945) to February 23 (1931). Greatest numbers are seen in November, December and January.

Usually appears in small flocks, but sometimes as many as 75-200 have been seen at one time.

HABITAT AND DISTRIBUTION—While most of the records come from east of Cleveland, the species probably occurs along the whole lakefront. Observations have been from White City, Fairport, and Lost Nation Airport (on Lost Nation Road near Lake Erie, Lake County). Often observed in company with snow buntings or horned larks.

SMITH'S LONGSPUR—Calcarius pictus (Swainson)

STATUS—Rare migrant.

There is a record of 2 birds of this species being shot from a large flock by Clark P. Streator at Garrettsville January 29, 1888 (Jones 1904a). It was also reported seen at Shaker Lake May 8, 1924, and at Ford Field (Western Reserve University) May 24, 1924, by Eastman, Kimmel and D. Hulme.

EASTERN SNOW BUNTING—Plectrophenax nivalis nivalis (Linnaeus)

Status—Not uncommon fall and winter visitor.

Earliest fall date—October 15, 1945. Average—November 5.

Latest spring date—March 14, 1948. Average—February 15.

Observed in compact flocks ranging from a few to approximately 2000 (December 25, 1930, Chardon) (Miller 1931). Sometimes associated with horned larks. Usually appears with the first arrival of snow.

Habitat and Distribution—This is a bird of the open spaces such as lake beaches, fields, golf courses, and airports, where it feeds on weed seeds above the snow. Often observed in cultivated fields that have been freshly manured. In this region it has been reported as seen along the Cleveland lakefront, White City, Fairport, Nela Park (East Cleveland), and open country in the suburbs and rural sections.

Literature Cited

ALDRICH, JOHN W.

1932 The Giant Red-wing in Ohio, The Auk 49:227.

1934 Observations on a Few Breeding Birds in Northeastern Ohio, Wilson Bulletin 46:96-103.

1936a Additions to the List of Ohio Birds, The Auk 53:98-99.

1936b European Woodcock (*Scolopax rusticola rusticola*) in Ohio, Ibid. 329-330.

1936c Sennett's Nighthawk in Ohio, Ibid. 333-334.

ALDRICH, JOHN W., and NUTT, DAVID C.

1939 Birds of Eastern Newfoundland, Scientific Publications of the Cleveland Museum of Natural History 4(2):13-42.

BAIRD, ROBERT L.

1932 The Season: Oberlin(Ohio) Region, Bird-Lore 34:14-16.

1934 The Season: Oberlin(Ohio) Region, Ibid. 36:183-184.

1936 The Season: Oberlin(Ohio) Region, Ibid. 38:468-470.

1937 The Season: Oberlin(Ohio) Region, Ibid. 39:169-170.

BAIRD, S. F.

1852 Description of a New Species of Sylvicola, Annals of the Lyceum of Natural History of New York 5:217-218.

BAIRD, S. F., BREWER, T. M., and RIDGWAY, R.

1874 A History of North American Birds . . . Land Birds, Boston: Little, Brown and Co., Vol. II.

BALDWIN, S. PRENTISS

1931 The Marriage Relations of the House Wren (*Troglodytes aedon*), Bird Banding by Systematic Trapping, Scientific Publications of the Cleveland Museum of Natural History 1(5):161-168.

BARROWS, WALTER B.

1889 The English Sparrow (*Passer domesticus*) in North America, U. S. Department of Agriculture, Division of Economic Ornithology and Mammalogy, Bulletin 1, Part II.

BENEDICT, MRS. HOWARD SMITH

1927 The Baltimore Oriole Wintering in Ohio, Wilson Bulletin 39:107.

BENT, A. C.
  1926 Life Histories of North American Marsh Birds, U. S.
       National Museum Bulletin No. 135.
  1927 Life Histories of North American Shore Birds, Ibid. No.
       142, Part I.
  1929 Life Histories of North American Shore Birds, Ibid. No.
       146, Part II.
  1948 Life Histories of North American Nuthatches, Wrens,
       Thrashers and Their Allies, Ibid. No. 195.
  1949 Life Histories of North American Thrushes, Kinglets,
       and Their Allies, Ibid. No. 196.

BOLE, B. P., JR.
  1937 First Breeding-Bird Census: Pine-Hemlock Forest, Bird-
       Lore 39:383-384.
  1938 Second Breeding-Bird Census: Upland Pine-Hemlock-
       Red Maple Forest, Ibid. 40:361.

BREWER, T. M.
  1859 Raptores and Fissirostres, North American Oology,
       Smithsonian Contributions to Knowledge, Vol. II, Part I.

CAMPBELL, LOUIS W.
  1940 Birds of Lucas County, Toledo Museum of Science Bul-
       letin, Toledo Zoological Society, Vol. 1, No. 1.
  1947 American Egrets Nesting on West Sister Island in Lake
       Erie, The Auk 64:461-462.

CHUBB, H. E.
  1880 Spring Field Notes, Forest and Stream 14:307.

COOK, ORANGE
  1909 A Bohemian Waxwing (*Ampelis garrulus*) in Ohio, Wil-
       son Bulletin 21:163.
  1915a The Prothonotary Warbler, Ibid. 27:349.
  1915b The Bewick Wren, Ibid. 349-350.

COOKE, WELLS W.
  1911 Distribution of the American Egrets, U. S. Department
       of Agriculture, Bureau of Biological Survey, Circular
       No. 84.

CRISTY, BAYARD H.
  1936 Kirtland Marginalia, The Cardinal 4(4):77-89.

Dawson, William L.
  1903 The Birds of Ohio, Columbus: Wheaton Publishing Co.

Doolittle, E. A.
  1914 Notes from Ohio, Bird-Lore 16:112.
  1916 Purple Sandpiper in Lake County, Ohio, Wilson Bulletin 28:197.
  1917a Notes from Lake County, Ohio, Ibid. 29:103.
  1917b Notes from Lake County, Ibid. 161-163.
  1918 Notes from Lake County, Ibid. 30:118-119.
  1919a Unusual Contents of a Mourning Dove's Nest, The Auk 36:281.
  1919b A Flight of Broad-winged Hawks and Roughlegs in Lake Co., Ohio, Ibid. 568.
  1919c Evening Grosbeak (*Hesperiphona v. vespertina*) in Ohio in May, Ibid. 574.
  1919d Notes from Lake County, Wilson Bulletin 31:27-28.
  1919e Notes from Lake County, Ibid. 127-129.
  1920a Notes from Lake County, Ibid. 32:65-67.
  1920b Notes from Lake County, Ibid. 98.
  1920c A May Evening Grosbeak in Lake County, Ibid. 98-99.
  1921 Notes from Lake County, Ibid. 33:34-35.
  1923a Breeding of Piping Plover in Lake Co., Ohio, The Auk 40:691.
  1923b Occurrence of Buff-breasted Sandpiper in Lake Co., Ohio, Ibid. 691-692.
  1924a Notes from Lake County, Wilson Bulletin 36:27.
  1919d Notes from Lake County, Wilson Bulletin 31:27-28.
  1924c Record of Brunnich's Murre for Lake Co., Ohio, The Auk 41:148.
  1926 The Blue Grosbeak in Lake County, Ohio, In Summer, Wilson Bulletin 38:157.
  1930 30th Christmas Census: Painesville, Ohio, Bird-Lore 32:50.
  1931 Bird Notes from Lake County, Ohio, Wilson Bulletin 43:225-227.
  1934 Nesting of Piping Plover in Northeastern Ohio, Oologist 51:7.
  1937 Oriole Lore, Ibid. 54:52-53.

GODFREY, W. EARL

    1943a Audubon's Warbler in Ohio, The Auk 60:451-452.

    1943b Eared Grebe in Ohio, Ibid. 452.

    1943c The Hoover Warbler in Ohio, Bird-Life 39(4):226.

HADELER, E. W.

    1924 Hudsonian Curlew in Lake County, Ohio, The Auk
        41:599-600.

    1930 Notes on Geese at Painesville, Ohio, Ibid. 47:552.

HALL, A.

    1883 Notes from Southampton, Mass., Ornithologist and
        Oologist 8(4):31-32.

HAMMETT, E. E., JR.

    1891 Black and White Creeper (*Mniotilta varia*), Oologist
        8(8):161.

HERSEY, F. SEYMOUR

    1917 The Status of the Black-throated Loon (*Gavia arctica*)
        as a North American Bird, The Auk 34:283-290.

HILL, RAYMOND W.

    1943 Purple Sandpipers at Richmond Beach, Ohio, Wilson
        Bulletin 55:128-129.

INGERSOLL, SEYMOUR R.

    1882 Spring Notes, Forest and Stream 18:305.

    1883 Birds of Northern Ohio, Ibid. 20:304-305.

    1884 Late Snipe, Ibid. 21:515.

JONES, LYNDS

    1897 Brunnich's Murre, *Uria lomvia*, on Lake Erie, Wilson
        Bulletin 4:16.

    1903 The Birds of Ohio, A Revised Catalogue, Ohio State
        Academy of Science Special Papers, No. 6.

    1904a An Addition to the Birds of Ohio, Wilson Bulletin
        16:85.

    1904b Additional Records of Ohio Birds, Ohio Naturalist
        4:112-113.

    1909 The Birds of Cedar Point and Vicinity, Wilson Bul-
        letin 21:115-131.

    1911 Exceptional Ohio Records, Ibid. 23:60-61.

KECK, J. M.
  1916 Native Wild Birds Observed in the City of Cleveland,
       The Bluebird 8(4):12-13.

KENDEIGH, S. CHARLES
  1924 The Season: Oberlin(Ohio) Region, Bird-Lore
       26:267-268.
  1925 The Season: Oberlin(Ohio) Region, Ibid. 27:340-341.
  1926 The Season: Oberlin(Ohio) Region, Ibid. 28:346-347.
  1934 The Role of Environment in the Life of Birds, Ecolog-
       ical Monographs 4:299-417.
  1941 Territorial and Mating Behavior of the House Wren,
       Illinois Biological Monographs 18(3):1-120.

KIRKPATRICK, JOHN
  1858a Natural History of the Birds of Ohio, Ohio Farmer
        7:147.
  1858b Natural History of the Birds of Ohio, Ibid. 8:107.
  1859 Descriptions of the Rapacious Birds of Ohio, 13th An-
       nual Report for the Year 1858, Ohio State Board of
       Agriculture, pp. 340-383.
  1860 Natural History of the Birds of Ohio, Ohio Farmer
       9:179.

KIRTLAND, JARED P.
  1838 Notes and Observations: Class II, Birds, Report on the
       Zoology of Ohio, Second Annual Report on the Geo-
       logical Survey of the State of Ohio, pp. 177-187.
  1850 Fragments of Natural History, Family Visitor 1(1):1.
  1851 New Habits of Birds, Family Visitor 2:68.
  1860 An Addition to the Fauna of Ohio, Ohio Farmer 9:91.
  1874a Peculiarities of Climate, Flora and Fauna of the South
        Shore of Lake Erie, in the Vicinity of Cleveland, Ohio,
        Proceedings of the Cleveland Academy of Natural
        Science, 1845-1859, pp. 165-171.
  1874b Mounted Birds From Northern Ohio, In the Academy's
        Museum, Ibid. 201-287.

LANGDON, FRANK W.
  1880 Ornithological Field Notes, with Five Additions to the
       Cincinnati Avian Fauna, Journal of the Cincinnati
       Society of Natural History 3(2):121-127.

MAYFIELD, HAROLD
  1943 The Season: Ohio-Michigan Region, Audubon Magazine 45:7-8.
  1944 The Season: Ohio-Michigan Region, Ibid. 46:5-6.
  1946 Audubon Field Notes: Ohio-Michigan Region, Ibid. 48:6-7.

MILLER, LYLE
  1930 The Chestnut-sided and Other Warblers Nesting in Geauga County, Ohio, Wilson Bulletin 42:56-57.
  1931 Bird-Lore's Thirty-first Christmas Census: Chardon, Ohio, Bird-Lore 33:58.

MOULTON, PHILLIPS
  1927 The Hooded Warbler Near Cleveland, Bird-Lore 29:121.

MOULTON, PHILLIPS, and DERBAUM, JACK
  1926 26th Christmas Census: Lakewood, Ohio, Bird-Lore 28:39.

PERRY, OLIVER HAZARD
  1899 Hunting Expeditions of Oliver Hazard Perry, For Private Distribution, Cleveland: The Marian Press.

PETERSON, ROGER T.
  1947 A Field Guide to the Birds, Second Revised and Enlarged Edition, Boston: Houghton Mifflin Company.

READ, M. C.
  1853a Birds of Ohio, Family Visitor 3:196-423.
  1853b Catalogue of the Birds of Northern Ohio, Proceedings of the Academy of Natural Science of Philadelphia 6(11):395-402.

RIDGWAY, ROBERT
  1916 The Birds of Northern and Middle America, U. S. National Museum Bulletin No. 50, Part VII.

SIMMONS, CAPT. GEORGE FINLAY
  1927 A Day with Bird Lovers of Cleveland, Your Garden 1:55-56.

SKAGGS, MERIT B.
  1941 Gambel's Sparrows in Ohio, Wilson Bulletin 53:242.
  1945 First Ohio Record of the Lark Bunting, The Auk 62:313.
  1948 Prothonotary Warblers Nesting Near Cleveland, Ohio, Jack-Pine Warbler 26(3):126.

SMITH, COL. JAMES
1907 Smith's Captivity with the Indians, Cincinnati: Robert Clark Co.

STEVENSON, J.
1931 An Old Record for the Western Meadowlark from Ohio, The Auk 48:431.

SWALES, BRADSHAW H.
1918 The Purple Sandpiper at Cleveland, Ohio, Occasional Papers of the Museum of Zoology, University of Michigan, No. 57.

TRAUTMAN, MILTON B.
1935 Notes on Some Ohio Birds, The Auk 52:201-202.

WALKER, C. F.
1937 The Season: Dayton(Ohio) Region, Bird-Lore 39:472-473.
1938a The Season: Dayton(Ohio) Region, Ibid. 40:152-153.
1938b The Season: Dayton(Ohio) Region, Ibid. 289-290.

WATTERSON, WILLIAM H.
1931 Audubon's Warbler in Northern Ohio, The Auk 48:435.

WHEATON, J. M.
1879a Kirtland's Warbler Again in Ohio, Bulletin of the Nuttall Ornithological Club 4:58.
1879b Occurrence of Birds Rare to the Vicinity of Columbus, O., Ibid. 62-63.
1882 Report on the Birds of Ohio, Report of the Geological Survey of Ohio, Vol. IV, Part I, Section 2, pp. 189-628.

WILLIAMS, ARTHUR B.
1947 11th Breeding-Bird Census: Climax Beech-Maple Forest with Some Hemlock (15 year summary), Audubon Field Notes 1(6):205-210.

WILSON, ALEXANDER
1828 American Ornithology, New York: Collins & Co., Vol. 1.

HISTORICAL

By ARTHUR B. WILLIAMS

The Arkites

INTEREST in the study of birds in our region, as we have indicated, goes back to the early days of Cleveland's history. In the period between 1830 and 1840 a group of young men met frequently in a small structure beside the home of Leonard Case, Sr., on the east side of Cleveland's Public Square, to discuss local natural history and study the collections which they gradually built up. Their small building they called the "Ark", and they referred to themselves as "Arkites". Some of them developed skill in taxidermy, and a collection of mounted birds was one of their special interests. A small glass case containing 8 of these specimens is in the possession of the Cleveland Museum of Natural History. The species represented are cardinal, orchard oriole, slate-colored junco, red-bellied woodpecker, sharp-shinned hawk, purple finch, Baltimore oriole and snow bunting. They are remarkably well preserved, considering the fact that more than 100 years have passed since they were prepared.

One of the most active of these amateur ornithologists was Rufus K. Winslow, whose name appears frequently in the foregoing pages as the authority for some rare early records. The wild turkey, mounted after Audubon's famous painting of this bird, shown at the beginning of this book, is the work of Winslow, and long adorned the mantelpiece in his dining room. Others who belonged to this early company of bird students were Leonard, Jr., and William Case, Capt. Ben Stannard and Dr. Elisha Sterling.

A painting, depicting a meeting of the Arkites, may be seen in the Library of the Western Reserve Historical Society.

Into this group, about 1837, to give it direction and inspiration, came Dr. Jared Potter Kirtland, lately arrived from Connecticut. Under the impetus of his leadership, the Cleveland Academy of Natural Science was organized November 24, 1845, to carry forward in a more orderly way the work of scientific research of those days. Of this body, Dr. Kirtland was president for 25 years. Reorganized May 15, 1869, it became the Kirtland Society of

Natural Sciences. This body in 1927 was merged with the Cleveland Museum of Natural History, which had been organized December 6, 1920. Thus we have an unbroken chain of organized interest in birds in Cleveland reaching back for over a century.

Early Cleveland Naturalists

Rufus K. Winslow (1817-1892) was a business man of early Cleveland who, following in his father's footsteps, became a shipbuilder and vessel owner. In 1869 he was president of the Kirtland Society of Natural Sciences. It is greatly to be regretted that Winslow never reduced his knowledge of the bird life of the region to writing. He was an ardent bird collector, and an expert taxidermist. He is so frequently quoted by others as the source of many important records, that it is apparent he was looked upon by his contemporaries, and by those immediately following him, as probably the foremost authority on the birds of the region during the period from about 1830 to 1885.

Dr. Jared P. Kirtland (1793-1877) was the great contemporary of Winslow. He came from Connecticut to the Western Reserve as a young physician about 1830, bought a farm at Rockport (now Lakewood), and lived there the rest of his life.[*] He was a man of many interests, including ornithology. He was a collector and an expert taxidermist. He was also a writer who left a wealth of early records on the natural history of the region. Appointed to have charge of the section devoted to zoology in the first geological survey of Ohio (published 1838), he contributed the first list of the birds of the state, including 222 species, of which more than two-thirds were new records. In 1850 he founded the magazine called *The Family Visitor*, in which many of his observations on the birds of the region were published.

M. C. Read, of Hudson, in 1853 was an associate of Kirtland's and followed him as editor of the *Family Visitor*. Read published a "Catalogue of the Birds of Northern Ohio" in 1853. This list included 145 species. It was "to be continued", but no further list appeared.

John Kirkpatrick (1819-1869) was born in Glasgow, Scotland, and came to Cleveland from Canada in 1843. For a long time he

---

[*] See The Lakewood Story, by Margaret M. Butler, Stratford House, N. Y. 1949, pp. 78-94.

was in the employ of the Cuyahoga Steam Furnace Company. He was later associated with the management of the *Ohio Farmer*. In 1866 he was appointed Superintendent of the Infirmary and Work House, which position he occupied until the time of his death in 1869. He was much respected for his sterling character and his humane attitude toward the incurably insane who were his wards. Kirkpatrick was deeply interested in natural science, and served for a time as secretary of the Cleveland Academy of Natural Science. His account of the ''Rapacious Birds of Ohio'' (hawks and owls) was originally written for, and published in the columns of the *Ohio Farmer* during 1858 and 1859. It was published in final form in the 13th Annual Report of the Ohio State Board of Agriculture in 1859. Of this work he says, ''Nearly all the species mentioned are described from specimens in the Museum of the Academy of Natural Science of Cleveland.''

Seymour Race Ingersoll (1860-1917) was a native Clevelander. His father was for many years treasurer of the C & P Railroad. Seymour Ingersoll's interest in birds is attested by the fact that he contributed a list of the ''Birds of Northern Ohio'' to *Forest and Stream* May 17, 1883. This list included 209 species, and in many instances the dates of arrival of migratory species are given. Since Ingersoll was a resident of Cleveland, his list is probably based largely on observations made in the Cleveland region, though this is not so stated.

Henry E. Chubb in 1869 was a bookkeeper for the Ohio and Pennsylvania Coal Company. Later he became secretary of the Cleveland Coal Exchange. He was apparently more interested in local ornithology than in the coal business, however, since in 1879 he is listed in the Cleveland Directory as a taxidermist doing business in the Benton Block at the west end of the Viaduct near Detroit Avenue. Wheaton refers to him as a ''well-known taxidermist and naturalist'' of Cleveland.

Until 1891, when he removed to New York, Chubb carried on his taxidermist business at the above address and became an often quoted authority on the birds of the region. Quickly following the publication of Ingersoll's list in *Forest and Stream* referred to above, Chubb added 44 more species to Ingersoll's list, and made certain comments and corrections with regard to 8 species reported by Ingersoll. Chubb says: ''These additions to the list published are made from actual capture or possession of species

187

mentioned, with four exceptions of which three are given above on the authority of R. K. Winslow, and prothonotary warbler which Dr. J. P. Kirtland showed me.'' Chubb also refers to himself in the above article as a collector of birds ''for about twenty years.'' This would include the period 1863 to 1883.

J. M. Keck was the minister of the Methodist Church in Mentor from 1883 to 1886, and again from 1890 to 1896. He was a ''co-operator'' of the U. S. Biological Survey, reporting regularly on his bird observations in the vicinity of Mentor, and also Cleveland, where he resided for a while. He was a contributor to the magazine *The Bluebird* (See page 191), in which he published an article on ''Native Wild Birds Observed in the City of Cleveland''. He frequently lectured on birds before school audiences.

Adrian A. Doolittle, known as ''Edward'' A. Doolittle (1876-1943), was a native of Painesville, and lived there all his life. He was an ardent bird student from young manhood, a keen observer, and kept full and accurate records, many of which he published in the *Wilson Bulletin*. He was a ''cooperator'' of the U. S. Biological Survey, and for a number of years operated a bird banding station in Painesville. His favorite places for studying birds were Mentor Marsh, Fairport Harbor and Grand River.

His occupation was that of a paper-hanger and interior decorator—a form of employment which made it possible for him to spend much of his time in the field. On his trips he usually preferred to go alone, though his close friend, Edward Hadeler, of Painesville, a man of similar tastes, sometimes accompanied him. The two often compared notes, and a sort of friendly rivalry existed between them.

Doolittle, besides being an outstanding field ornithologist, was an authority on the reptiles and plants of the region, and had an extensive collection of Indian and mound builder materials.

Charles M. Shipman (1874-1947) was born in New York City, received his early education at Hasbrouck Institute, and his professional training (in chemistry) at Stevens Institute of Technology. He came to Willoughby from the Oakland Chemical Company, Staten Island, New York, to be associated with the J. H. R. Products Company here.

About 1925 he retired from active business to devote his time to nature photography, lecturing on outdoor subjects, and the promotion of conservation projects.

Shipman was for many years president of the Burroughs Nature Club of Willoughby, an organization which included in its membership many people from Greater Cleveland, as well as from all parts of Lake County. He was the first president of the Cleveland Bird Club, and later was instrumental in securing the Hach Sanctuary for the club. He assisted Dr. Francis H. Herrick in his famous studies of the American Eagle at Vermilion. He was a constant champion of the hawks and owls against persecution and indiscriminate slaughter.

His lectures on birds and other forms of wildlife were illustrated with exquisitely beautiful hand-colored lantern slides, which he made from his own photographs. He was a popular speaker in the public schools, and before various clubs and other organizations, and in this way reached many thousands of people with his stirring message.

IN THE FIELD of scientific ornithological research the names of two Clevelanders stand out prominently.

Dr. Francis Hobart Herrick (1858-1940) founded the Department of Biology of Western Reserve University and was its head from 1888 to 1929. He was a trustee of the Cleveland Museum of Natural History from the time of its organization in 1920 until his death in 1940.

Dr. Herrick was a pioneer in the study of bird behaviour, and in the use of the camera and blind as an aid to such studies. His book, "The Home Life of Wild Birds" (1901), described the methods which he worked out, and pointed the way for many other such studies. He became the best biographer of John James Audubon. His book, "Audubon the Naturalist—a History of His Life and Times" (1917), based largely on original material which he discovered abroad, is the most authoritative of all Audubon biographies. His ten year study of the bald eagle, "The American Eagle" (1934), made with the aid of a blind located atop a steel tower near the eagle's nest, is one of the classics of ornithological literature. Finally, "Wild Birds at Home" (1935) incorporated much of Herrick's philosophy regarding bird behaviour and instinct.

Not the least of Herrick's contributions to our knowledge of local ornithology was the starting of the *Cleveland Bird Calendar* in 1905 (See page 3).

Dr. Samuel Prentiss Baldwin (1868-1938) was a lawyer by profession, but an ornithologist by inclination.

He was admitted to the Ohio bar in 1894 and practiced in Cleveland until 1902, when ill health forced him to retire. He then devoted his time largely to the study of birds. He was a trustee of the Cleveland Museum of Natural History from the date of its organization to the time of his death.

Beginning in 1914 he was among the first to develop the techniques of bird banding for scientific study. On his estate at Gates Mills, overlooking the Chagrin Valley, he established the Baldwin Bird Research Laboratory. Here, with Dr. S. Charles Kendeigh and other workers, he carried on extensive and detailed studies of the house wren, as well as of other birds. During the course of a season as many as 2000 live birds would be thus handled and studied by him and his assistants.

By the use of a device known as a potentiometer, and other instruments, a mechanical recording of nesting activities was made possible, covering every minute of the day. His championship of the cause of hawks and owls in Ohio was spirited and productive of results.

Baldwin's contributions to the literature of scientific ornithology were many. Among the more important were "Bird Banding by Systematic Trapping" (1931), "Measurements of Birds" (with Harry C. Oberholser and Leonard G. Worley, 1931), "The Physiology of the Temperature of Birds" (with S. C. Kendeigh, 1932), "The Protection of Hawks and Owls in Ohio" (with S. C. Kendeigh and Roscoe W. Franks, 1932).

WE WOULD NOT do justice to Cleveland's reputation as a center of ornithological interest if we did not mention the names of certain other citizens or former citizens of Greater Cleveland still living, who have, by their work here and elsewhere helped to advance the cause of scientific ornithology. Among them are such well known names as the following:

Dr. Harry C. Oberholser, formerly Senior Biologist, U. S. Fish and Wildlife Service; Dr. Herbert W. Brandt, founder of the Cleveland Bird Research Foundation; Dr. John W. Aldrich, Biologist in Charge, Section of Distribution and Migration of Birds, Branch of Wildlife Research, U. S. Fish and Wildlife Service; W. Earl Godfrey, Biologist, National Museum of Canada;

Don Eckelberry, bird artist and illustrator for "Audubon Bird Guide" and other publications.

Organized Interest in Birds

The Cleveland Bird Lovers' Association was organized in October 1914 by Mrs. Elizabeth C. T. Miller. At that time it had about 200 members, and published a magazine, *The Bluebird,* which was owned and edited by Mrs. Miller. The objectives of the Association were stated as "bird protection and conservation". A program of lectures before schools and civic clubs was undertaken; exhibits were planned; bird houses, books and charts were sold. The Association apparently became a war casualty in 1918.

The S. Louise Patteson Memorial Association was organized April 21, 1923, by Mrs. Stella M. Antisdale, for the purpose of obtaining and erecting a symbolic statue of "Spring" in memory of S. Louise Patteson, a devoted lover of the birds. The statue, now in the Fine Arts Garden, stood for a number of years in the area between Coventry Road and the lower Shaker Lake, then a City of Cleveland park. In 1928 the Association changed its name to become the Cleveland Bird Club.

The Cleveland Bird Club was an outgrowth of the S. Louise Patteson Memorial Association as indicated above. In May, 1928, by a change of name and an enlargement and widening of its objectives, the Memorial Association became The Cleveland Bird Club. The Club was incorporated March 13, 1941. It is affiliated with the National Audubon Society. Its activities now include the conduct of field trips for its over 1200 members; an extensive series of annual lectures open to the public; the ownership and maintenance of three bird sanctuaries; the holding of an annual exhibit of birds and other wildlife; the conduct of an annual birdhouse building contest in connection with The Cleveland Home and Flower Show; and an outstanding movie-lecture on conservation offered annually to a county-wide group of school children. As indicated on page 3 from 1931 to 1943 the Club shared the responsibility for the publication of *The Cleveland Bird Calendar.*

The Herrick Ornithological Society was an organization of students in the Department of Biology, Western Reserve University, active from 1939 to 1941. Its members were interested especially in field studies of birds, and made two surveys of wintering waterfowl along the Lake Erie shore (See page 6).

The Kirtland Society was organized within the Cleveland Museum of Natural History in 1940 to provide an opportunity for adults to associate themselves together for the promotion of amateur research in the various fields of natural history. The first division of the Kirtland Society to become active was the Kirtland Bird Club.

The Kirtland Bird Club has placed emphasis on field work. Since 1940 it has organized and conducted the Annual Christmas Bird Counts for the Cleveland region; it has furnished volunteer leadership of a high quality for the popular spring "Bird Walks" sponsored by the Cleveland Museum of Natural History; it has produced a voluminous record of seasonal observations on birds, which it publishes four times a year as issues of the *Cleveland Bird Calendar;* it has conducted extensive studies of the wintering waterfowl population along the Lake Erie shore in the vicinity of Cleveland. Individual members have made numerous studies of breeding bird populations and winter woodland bird populations within the region, covering some 51 different areas representative of the various types of nesting habitats within the region (See pages 5-6).

The Cleveland Museum of Natural History—As indicated on page 186, the Museum of Natural History is the lineal descendant of groups of people interested in birds since the early days of Cleveland's history. Organized in December 1920, the Museum established its Department of Ornithology early in 1923. Under the eye of Dr. Harry C. Oberholser as advisor, the assembly of a collection of bird skins for scientific study was begun. This collection now numbers some 55,000 specimens, and includes the finest series of bird skins in existence from certain important areas. It has the only collection in the world on the basis of which careful technical work on the birds of Ohio can be done.

Among the first exhibits shown when the Museum was opened to the public was an Ohio Bird Room, and this, in amplified form, continues to be one of the most popular of its exhibits. Since 1934 the Museum has conducted a series of popular Sunday morning Bird Walks during the season of the spring migration. It issues both popular and scientific publications dealing with birds. In the outdoor programs which center about its Trailside Museums in the City and Metropolitan Parks, much emphasis is given to the interpretation of the bird life of the Cleveland region.

Place Names Frequently Mentioned in the Text

ABRAM'S LAKE—A small body of water enclosed within the area bounded by Bagley, Engle, Five Points, and Eastland Roads in Brook Park Village. Formerly included much swampy land extending to eastern edge of the present Cleveland Airport.

AKRON LAKES—A series of small lakes in the vicinity of Akron, some of which lie just outside the 30-mile limit defined as the Cleveland region, but are included as explained on page 7. The principal ones are Lake Dorothy, Barberton Reservoir, Summit Lake, Portage Lakes, Nimisilla Lake, Wingfoot Lake, Mogadore Reservoir, Stafford Lake.

AURORA BIRD SANCTUARY—A tract of 161.4 acres in the Village of Aurora, containing a small lake. Owned and administered by the Cleveland Bird Club.

AURORA POND—A small postglacial lake southeast of Cleveland near the Village of Aurora, formerly supporting a tamarack bog at its northerly end. Here also are remnants of a yellow birch-black ash-red maple swamp forest. Also referred to as Solon Bog.

BALDWIN BIRD RESEARCH LABORATORY—Mayfield Road, Gates Mills Village, at the top of the west valley wall.

BEAVER CREEK — A small stream entering Lake Erie in Lorain County at the extreme western edge of our region.

BEDFORD—The Bedford Reservation of the Cleveland Metropolitan Park System, 1203 acres, including the spectacular gorge of Tinker's Creek. Remnants of oak-hickory, beech-maple, hemlock and flood plain forests are to be found here.

BLACK BROOK—At the eastern edge of Mentor Marsh in the Village of Richmond.

BRADLEY POND—Just southwest of Burton, Geauga County, on the headwaters of the Cuyahoga River.

BRECKSVILLE—The Brecksville Reservation of the Cleveland Metropolitan Park System, 1784 acres. Excellent remnants of former extensive white oak stands, oak-hickory ridges, and ravine slopes supporting beech-maple and associated species, are found here. A deep gorge with hemlocks is a feature of the reservation.

CLAGUE POND—In the Village of Westlake, west of Cleveland.

CLEVELAND METROPOLITAN PARK SYSTEM—Surrounding the City of Cleveland and Cuyahoga County in a great semicircle of reservations and connecting parkways, the Metropolitan Park System has created what amounts to a great wildlife sanctuary of over 13,000 acres in extent. Included within it are some fine remnants of native forest types, as well as open fields and meadows, river edge, lakes and ponds. Occupying sites on the lake plain and the plateau, and including river valleys as well as highlands, these reservations provide a variety of habitats attractive to birds. All wildlife in these reservations is fully protected. The various reservations are listed herein separately.

CLIFTON BEACH-CLIFTON PARK—On the Lake Erie shore on the east side of the mouth of Rocky River.

CORNING LAKE—A small artificial lake on the Holden Arboretum grounds.

DOAN BROOK — A small stream rising in the City of Shaker Heights, including the Shaker Lakes, and emptying into Lake Erie at Gordon Park.

EDGEWATER PARK—On the Lake Erie shore, City of Cleveland, just west of the Cuyahoga River.

ELY PARK-ELY WOODS—A city park of the City of Elyria, on the east side of the Black River. An area of fairly wild river bottomland.

FAIRMOUNT RESERVOIR—At the corner of Fairmount and Baldwin Roads, Cleveland.

FAIRPORT HARBOR — At the mouth of the Grand River, which empties into Lake Erie in the far northeastern corner of our region.

194

FOREST HILL PARK—Lies partly in the City of East Cleveland, partly in the City of Cleveland Heights. Includes 235 acres of fields, woodlands and playfields.

GORDON PARK—City of Cleveland. On the Lake Erie shore at about East 73rd Street. Here a power plant of the Cleveland Electric Illuminating Company empties warm water into the lake, thus maintaining a considerable space of open water even in severe winter weather.

HINCKLEY-HINCKLEY LAKE — The Hinckley Reservation of the Cleveland Metropolitan Park System, 1154 acres, 20 miles south of Cleveland in Medina County.

HOLDEN ARBORETUM—A tract of over 280 acres east of Cleveland, near Little Mountain, containing some excellent remnants of beech-maple-hemlock forest communities, and some natural secondary succession areas. Much experimental planting to produce ecological units not native to the region has been done. A chain of small ponds and bogs has been created here which are very attractive to birds.

LAKE DOROTHY—See Akron Lakes.

LAKE ERIE SHORE—Lake Erie stands at 573 feet above sea level. The shore line from Beaver Creek on the west, to Fairport Harbor at the mouth of the Grand River on the east, is included in the region. This provides an opportunity for the observation not only of many birds of the open waters, but also many migrating land birds following the lake shore as a flyway.

LAKE ROCKWELL—See Akron Lakes.

LAKEVIEW CEMETERY—In the City of East Cleveland. Lies between Euclid Avenue and Mayfield Road.

LITTLE MOUNTAIN—A small, saddle-shaped hill lying partly in Lake, partly in Geauga County, to the east of Cleveland, on which are extensive remnants of a boreal forest of white pine and hemlock. Elevation 1260 feet above sea level. The sandstone "ledges" here have developed deep crevasses which sometimes hold snow in their depths throughout July.

MENTOR HEADLANDS—On Lake Erie, west of the Village of Richmond.

MENTOR MARSH—The former mouth of the Grand River, extending westerly from Richmond, including some open water at its eastern and western ends, with a lowland swamp forest in between. Portions may become a state park.

MOGADORE RESERVOIR—See Akron Lakes.

MOSQUITO CREEK—A reservoir on a tributary of the Mahoning River north of Warren in Trumbull County.

NORTH CHAGRIN—The North Chagrin Reservation of the Cleveland Metropolitan Park System, 1497 acres, about 16 miles east of the Cleveland city limits. Contains some excellent examples of beech-maple-hemlock forest, together with 2 small ponds and a considerable planting of pines and spruces.

NORTH CHAGRIN POND—A small pond, sometimes referred to as "Sunset Pond", in the southwest corner of the North Chagrin Reservation, just off SOM Center Road.

PYMATUNING RESERVOIR—Lying partly in Ohio, partly in Pennsylvania, directly east of the Village of Andover in Ashtabula County.

RICHMOND BEACH—Just west of Fairport on the Lake Erie shore. About the only sand beach of any extent in the region. Shortly to become a state park.

ROCKEFELLER PARK—City of Cleveland. The connecting link between Wade Park and Gordon Park.

ROCKY RIVER—The Rocky River Reservation of the Cleveland Metropolitan Park System. A narrow winding parkway about 20 miles long, including most of the valley of Rocky River and large areas along its east branch. 4296 acres. Typical northern Ohio flood plain forests are a feature of the lower course of the river, while the upper valley and the east branch include some fine examples of beech-maple forest.

SHAKER LAKES—Two small artificial lakes lying between the Cities of Cleveland Heights and Shaker Heights, east of Cleveland. A part of the park systems of the two cities. A good place to see warblers during migration.

SHERWIN POND—On the private estate of Francis Sherwin at Waite Hill, south of Willoughby. Migrating ducks, geese and swans regularly stop here.

SOLON BOG—See Aurora Pond.

SOUTH CHAGRIN—The South Chagrin Reservation of the Cleveland Metropolitan Park System, 509 acres, is situated about 10 miles south of North Chagrin on the edge of the gorge of the Aurora Branch of the Chagrin River. It contains some good remnants of beech-maple-hemlock forest, together with much second growth and some pine and spruce plantings.

STEBBIN'S GULCH—A deep, cool, spectacular ravine, tributary to the East Branch of the Chagrin River, south of Little Mountain, in which remnants of northern vegetation, such as hemlock and mountain maple, still persist.

SUMMIT LAKE—See Akron Lakes.

TERMINAL TOWER — 708 feet high; on the southwest corner of Cleveland's Public Square.

WADE PARK-WADE PARK POND—In the valley of Doan Brook just north of Euclid Avenue at East Park Boulevard.

WAITE HILL—The Village of Waite Hill, south of Willoughby, including Sherwin Pond, which see.

WHITE CITY—On the Lake Erie shore at about East 142nd Street, Cleveland. The site of a former amusement park of this name. Shorebirds, gulls and terns may be seen to advantage here.

WINGFOOT LAKE—See Akron Lakes.

Composite List of 106 Species Reported Seen on Christmas Bird Counts 1910-1948

Loon
Holboell's Grebe
Horned Grebe
Pied-billed Grebe
Gannet
Double-crested Cormorant
Great Blue Heron
Canada Goose
Mallard
Black Duck
Gadwall
Baldpate
American Pintail
Green-winged Teal
Shoveller
Redhead
Ring-necked Duck
Canvasback
Lesser Scaup
American Goldeneye
Bufflehead
Oldsquaw
White-winged Scoter
Ruddy Duck
Hooded Merganser
American Merganser
Red-breasted Merganser
Sharp-shinned Hawk
Cooper's Hawk
Red-tailed Hawk
Red-shouldered Hawk
Rough-legged Hawk
Bald Eagle
Marsh Hawk
Pigeon Hawk
Sparrow Hawk

Ruffed Grouse
Bobwhite
Ring-necked Pheasant
Coot
Killdeer
Purple Sandpiper
Iceland Gull
Herring Gull
Ring-billed Gull
Franklin's Gull
Bonaparte's Gull
Rock Dove
Mourning Dove
Screech Owl
Great Horned Owl
Snowy Owl
Barred Owl
Belted Kingfisher
Flicker
Pileated Woodpecker
Red-bellied Woodpecker
Red-headed Woodpecker
Yellow-bellied Sapsucker
Hairy Woodpecker
Downy Woodpecker
Prairie Horned Lark
Blue Jay
Crow
Black-capped Chickadee
Tufted Titmouse
White-breasted Nuthatch
Red-breasted Nuthatch
Brown Creeper
Winter Wren
Carolina Wren
Mockingbird

Catbird
Robin
Hermit Thrush
Bluebird
Golden-crowned Kinglet
Ruby-crowned Kinglet
Bohemian Waxwing
Cedar Waxwing
Northern Shrike
Starling
Myrtle Warbler
English Sparrow
Meadowlark
Red-winged Blackbird
Rusty Blackbird
Bronzed Grackle
Cowbird

Cardinal
Evening Grosbeak
Purple Finch
Pine Grosbeak
Common Redpoll
Pine Siskin
Goldfinch
Red Crossbill
Red-eyed Towhee
Slate-colored Junco
Tree Sparrow
Field Sparrow
White-throated Sparrow
Swamp Sparrow
Song Sparrow
Lapland Longspur
Snow Bunting

List of Species Observed in Downtown Cleveland

131 species of birds observed on or over the grounds of the Cleveland Museum of Natural History, 2717 Euclid Avenue, and adjoining properties 1941-1943.

Great Blue Heron
American Bittern
Least Bittern
Canada Goose
Red-breasted Merganser
Duck Hawk
Sparrow Hawk
Bobwhite
Ring-necked Pheasant
Killdeer
American Woodcock
Wilson's Snipe
Herring Gull
Ring-billed Gull
Bonaparte's Gull
Common Tern
Mourning Dove
Rock Dove
Yellow-billed Cuckoo
Black-billed Cuckoo
Screech Owl
Whip-poor-will
Nighthawk
Chimney Swift
Ruby-throated Hummingbird
Belted Kingfisher
Flicker
Red-headed Woodpecker
Yellow-bellied Sapsucker
Hairy Woodpecker
Downy Woodpecker
Kingbird
Crested Flycatcher

Phoebe
Yellow-bellied Flycatcher
Acadian Flycatcher
Alder Flycatcher
Least Flycatcher
Wood Pewee
Tree Swallow
Bank Swallow
Rough-winged Swallow
Barn Swallow
Purple Martin
Blue Jay
Crow
Black-capped Chickadee
White-breasted Nuthatch
Red-breasted Nuthatch
Brown Creeper
House Wren
Mockingbird
Catbird
Brown Thrasher
Robin
Wood Thrush
Hermit Thrush
Olive-backed Thrush
Gray-cheeked Thrush
Veery
Bluebird
Golden-crowned Kinglet
Ruby-crowned Kinglet
Cedar Waxwing
Migrant Shrike
Starling

Yellow-throated Vireo
Blue-headed Vireo
Red-eyed Vireo
Philadelphia Vireo
Warbling Vireo
Black and White Warbler
Blue-winged Warbler
Tennessee Warbler
Orange-crowned Warbler
Nashville Warbler
Parula Warbler
Yellow Warbler
Magnolia Warbler
Cape May Warbler
Black-throated Blue Warbler
Myrtle Warbler
Black-throated Green Warbler
Cerulean Warbler
Blackburnian Warbler
Chestnut-sided Warbler
Bay-breasted Warbler
Black-poll Warbler
Pine Warbler
Palm Warbler
Ovenbird
Grinnell's Waterthrush
Louisiana Waterthrush
Connecticut Warbler
Mourning Warbler
Northern Yellowthroat
Yellow-breasted Chat
Wilson's Warbler
Canada Warbler

Redstart
English Sparrow
Bobolink
Meadowlark
Red-winged Blackbird
Baltimore Oriole
Rusty Blackbird
Bronzed Grackle
Cowbird
Scarlet Tanager
Cardinal
Rose-breasted Grosbeak
Indigo Bunting
Purple Finch
Common Redpoll
Goldfinch
Red-eyed Towhee
Savannah Sparrow
Grasshopper Sparrow
Henslow's Sparrow
Vesper Sparrow
Slate-colored Junco
Tree Sparrow
Chipping Sparrow
Field Sparrow
White-crowned Sparrow
White-throated Sparrow
Fox Sparrow
Lincoln's Sparrow
Swamp Sparrow
Song Sparrow
Snow Bunting

List of 115 Species Included in Breeding Bird Population Studies

Pied-billed Grebe
Green Heron
American Bittern
Least Bittern
Canada Goose
Mallard
Black Duck
Wood Duck
Turkey Vulture
Sharp-shinned Hawk
Cooper's Hawk
Red-tailed Hawk
Red-shouldered Hawk
Broad-winged Hawk
Marsh Hawk
Sparrow Hawk
Ruffed Grouse
Bobwhite
Ring-necked Pheasant
Virginia Rail
Sora
Florida Gallinule
Killdeer
Woodcock
Upland Plover
Spotted Sandpiper
Rock Dove
Mourning Dove
Yellow-billed Cuckoo
Black-billed Cuckoo
Screech Owl
Great Horned Owl
Barred Owl
Whip-poor-will
Nighthawk
Chimney Swift

Ruby-throated Hummingbird
Belted Kingfisher
Flicker
Pileated Woodpecker
Red-bellied Woodpecker
Red-headed Woodpecker
Hairy Woodpecker
Downy Woodpecker
Kingbird
Crested Flycatcher
Phoebe
Acadian Flycatcher
Alder Flycatcher
Least Flycatcher
Wood Pewee
Horned Lark
Tree Swallow
Rough-winged Swallow
Barn Swallow
Purple Martin
Blue Jay
Crow
Black-capped Chickadee
Tufted Titmouse
White-breasted Nuthatch
Red-breasted Nuthatch
House Wren
Carolina Wren
Long-billed Marsh Wren
Short-billed Marsh Wren
Catbird
Brown Thrasher
Robin
Wood Thrush
Veery
Bluebird

Blue-gray Gnatcatcher
Cedar Waxwing
Starling
Yellow-throated Vireo
Blue-headed Vireo
Red-eyed Vireo
Warbling Vireo
Prothonotary Warbler
Blue-winged Warbler
Yellow Warbler
Black-throated Green Warbler
Cerulean Warbler
Blackburnian Warbler
Ovenbird
Grinnell's Waterthrush
Louisiana Waterthrush
Northern Yellowthroat
Yellow-breasted Chat
Hooded Warbler
American Redstart
English Sparrow
Bobolink

Meadowlark
Red-winged Blackbird
Baltimore Oriole
Bronzed Grackle
Cowbird
Scarlet Tanager
Cardinal
Rose-breasted Grosbeak
Indigo Bunting
Purple Finch
Goldfinch
Red-eyed Towhee
Savannah Sparrow
Grasshopper Sparrow
Henslow's Sparrow
Vesper Sparrow
Slate-colored Junco
Chipping Sparrow
Field Sparrow
Swamp Sparrow
Song Sparrow

Index of Common and Scientific Names

H

I

J

ADDITIONS OR CORRECTIONS

ADDITIONS OR CORRECTIONS